Nature Library
PREHISTORIC LIFE

Nature Library
PREHISTORIC LIFE

Richard Moody

Exeter Books

NEW YORK

Artists

Victor Ambrus; Max Ansell; J. Baker; John Barber; Ray and Corinne Burrows; Jim Channell-Linden Artists; Ralph S. Coventry Associates; Design Practitioners Ltd; The Garden Studio; Hayward Art Group; Kim Ludlow; Dougal MacDougal; Bob Mathias; Tony Morris; E. Murphy; James Nicholls; David Nockels; Pat Oxenham; Linda Parry; Eric Robson; John Smith; George Thompson; Peter Thornley; Tudor Art Agency Ltd; P. Turner; Maurice Wilson; Michael Youens.

Copyright © Newnes Books 1983
London · New York · Sydney · Toronto
Astronaut House, Hounslow Road, Feltham, Middlesex, England

First published in USA 1983 by Exeter Books
Distributed by Bookthrift
Exeter is a trademark of Simon & Schuster
Bookthrift is a registered trademark of Simon & Schuster
New York, New York

ISBN 0-671-05924-8

Printed in Italy

Photographic acknowledgements

BIOFOTOS, FARNHAM 26; DONALD BROOM, READING 46; HERVE CHAUMETON, CHAMALIERES 12 bottom, 25 top left, 57, 69 right; ADRIAN DAVIES, WALLINGTON 67; HAMLYN GROUP PICTURE LIBRARY 33, 75; INSTITUTE OF GEOLOGICAL SCIENCES, LONDON 61 top left, 62 bottom right, 65 centre, 65 right; MANSELL COLLECTION, LONDON 17 top right, 17 bottom; N.A.S.A., WASHINGTON 9; NATIONAL PORTRAIT GALLERY, LONDON 17 top left; OXFORD SCIENTIFIC FILMS 69 left; R.I.D.A., NORBITON 71 left, 74, David Bayliss 6 – 7, 12 top, 22, 25 top centre, 25 top right, 25 bottom, 27 top left, 27 top right, 27 bottom, 28, 29 top left, 29 top right, 29 bottom, 30, 51 left, 58, 59, 60 top, 60 bottom, 61 top right, 61 bottom, 62 top right, 62 left, 65 left, 68 top, 68 bottom, 71 right, 73 top, 73 bottom, 76 – 77, R. T. J. Moody 40, 51 right, Sinclair Stammers 15, B. Wood 53, 54 – 55; Roger Viollet, Paris 16 left; R. C. L. WILSON, BERKHAMPSTEAD 20.

Contents

Foreword

Scientists believe the Earth was formed approximately 4·5 billion years ago. We cannot be exactly sure when the first life forms appeared, but it is thought primitive micro-organisms evolved about 3·5 billion years ago, and during the next 2·5 – 3·0 billion years, simple life forms gradually developed. From about 570 million years ago until the present day, the geological record reveals the progressive, often explosive, development of animal and plant life to the level we see today.

Such knowledge is derived from the incomplete fossil record. Through the vagaries of preservation, certain organisms are rarely or never preserved and thus some information is lost to the geologist forever. Soft-bodied animals are particularly susceptible and, except under special circumstances, rarely leave any trace of their form. Marine organisms are most commonly preserved as fossils, as conditions on the seafloor are usually favorable for the preservation of dead organisms.

Sedimentary rocks provide a valuable insight into ancient terrestrial and marine environments. The study of modern environments enables geologists to determine accurately the conditions and broad environmental settings in which these rocks, originally soft muds and sands, were deposited. By combining this information with data from the fossil record, we can reconstruct not only the relationships which existed between the animals and the environments in which presumably they lived, but also between the animal communities themselves.

Palaeontological studies continually reveal exciting discoveries of previously undescribed fossils and so many of our theories and ideas pertaining to palaeontology are constantly being refined and modified.

Introduction

The Earth was formed 4·6 billion years ago, but over a billion years passed before life in its simplest forms appeared. Therefore, before thinking about fossils, it is useful to focus our minds on the complex nature of the ancient masses that form the cores of the continents. These rocks have been subjected to many episodes of folding, erosion, burial and alteration and their textures and fabrics require sophisticated interpretations. The same is true of fossils, yet it is these remains of plants and animals that provide much of our current information on the evolution of the biosphere.

The biosphere is unique to our planet. It is an organic realm within which myriads of plants and animals have adapted to specific environmental conditions. The biosphere and its development is closely

Primeval Earth contained the essential elements of life whose fusion was enhanced by lightning and the absence of oxygen.

interwoven with the origin of our planet and the formation of the various zones that comprise it.

When the solar system was formed 4·6 billion years ago, clouds of gas and solids first rotated and then accreted around the Sun to form planets. The Earth itself formed when numerous minute bodies fused together. Internally, the temperature of the new planet increased and differentiation took place into the physical zones: the core, mantle and crust; and later, with the separation of gases and water, the hydrosphere and atmosphere. For millions of years the Earth's surface and atmosphere were unsuitable for life, but the right constituents were present to trigger the production of amino acids, fatty acids and urea. These are the building blocks of life and, strangely, their development was made possible by the absence of free oxygen in the earliest atmosphere. Under present atmospheric conditions, the chemicals of life would have been quickly degraded.

The first amino acids and sugars probably appeared between 4 and 3·5 billion years ago. In time they combined to form complex polymers, or proteins, some of which became enclosed in their own protective membranes. Although they were not living organisms they survived within their own protected environment and when too large subdivided into 'daughter' units.

Some doubt exists as to the form and appearance of the first living organisms. Recently, scientists have reinterpreted some of the earliest described 'organisms' as the possible infill of microfractures in Precambrian rocks by later algal material. Other evidence persists however, and large dividing cells are recorded from rocks billions of years old. In fact, algal mounds or stromatolites similar to those found in Sharks Bay, South Australia, grew in the shallow seas which covered parts of Canada and Africa over 2 billion years ago. These mounds were formed by blue-green algae and their appearance must have provided the first obvious signs of the evolving biosphere.

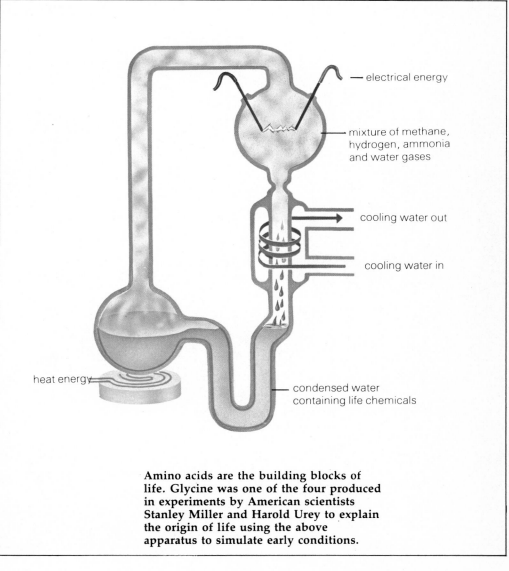

— electrical energy

— mixture of methane, hydrogen, ammonia and water gases

cooling water out

cooling water in

heat energy

— condensed water containing life chemicals

Amino acids are the building blocks of life. Glycine was one of the four produced in experiments by American scientists Stanley Miller and Harold Urey to explain the origin of life using the above apparatus to simulate early conditions.

How fossils are formed

Fossils are the remains of dead organisms that once lived on the surface of our planet. They may be the mineralised hard parts of animals such as clams, insects or vertebrates or just impressions of soft-bodied creatures like jellyfish. Fossils may be preserved in many ways with the oldest forms invariably losing their original mineral composition or structure. More recent organisms from the last 50 or 60 million years may sometimes retain their original skeletal composition but most, like their more ancient counterparts, will be either recrystallised or replaced mineralogically. Recrystallisation involves an ion for ion exchange within the skeleton which results in a coarser, perhaps heavier, structure. Where the original minerals are dissolved and replaced by new minerals the fossil may have an enhanced beauty: silica and iron pyrites are common replacement minerals. Many fossils consist of the original hard parts of the animal as well as minerals taken from the surrounding rocks. In this process, known as petrifaction, a fossil's structure will be preserved but its hardness and weight will

Creation of a fossil shell

living animal

hard parts of dead animal

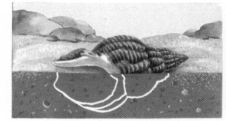
rapid burial

impregnation by minerals from sediments

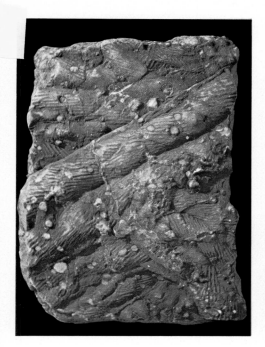

Above: **A trace fossil, *Cruziana*. These are the tracks made by trilobites and trilobite-like arthropods. Over thirty species of these tracks have been recognised.**

A fossil brachiopod illustrating replacement by pyrite.

increase. This is what has happened to the bivalve *Carbonicola* shown below. Organisms of an organic or chitinous nature, including plant debris such as *Odontopteris*, and the now extinct graptolites may be preserved as carbonaceous films. This is known as carbonization and is due to a reduction or distillation of the original tissues so that the hydrogen, oxygen and nitrogen constituents are decreased relative to carbon.

Many fossils buried over a long period of time are lost by the action of water percolating through the enclosing rock. The solution of their skeletons may therefore leave a void or space which is recognisable as an *external mould* of the original organism. (An example is the ammonoid *Goniatites* shown below). Often, as in the case of clams, the shell is infilled with sediment before solution. This infill represents an *internal mould*; it may retain all the form and markings of the inner surface. With the disappearance of the original shell such internal moulds, or 'stone kernels', may be easily collected.

In general terms the modes of preservation noted above are linked with body fossils, the remains of animals or plants. Palaeontologists also study the tracks, trails, burrows, borings and faecal deposits of organisms and these *trace-fossils* are usually preserved as impressions, casts or simply holes in the sediment.

Opposite: **Sometimes fossil woods are preserved in arid environments where the tissues become impregnated with silica. These fossils can still show the growth rings as can be seen in this section of petrified wood from Arizona.**

The fossil *Hoplites*, a medium-sized ammonite. The original remains of the organism have been replaced by iron pyrites giving it an enhanced appearance.

Four types of fossil. The chances that an organism will be fossilized are greatly increased if it has hard parts, such as a shell, but even these are frequently broken down by scavengers, bacterial action and weathering. Therefore rapid burial in a suitable substrate is necessary.

coal-measure plant
Odontopteris

ammonite
Goniatites

footprint

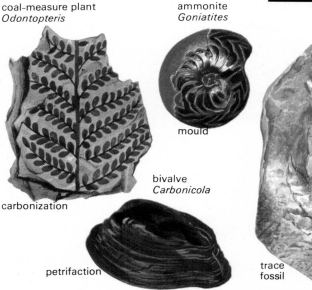

mould

bivalve
Carbonicola

carbonization

petrifaction

trace
fossil

Fossils and geology

Both trace fossils and body fossils can be used in the interpretation of ancient environments and particularly with the role of specific organisms in a community and with the factors that controlled their life and distribution. Fossils also provide us with a tool for the correlation of rock strata since the presence of different fossils is important in establishing the correct sequence of rock layers on a world-wide basis. Fossils such as graptolites, ammonites and foraminiferids change rapidly with time and if a species is both time-restricted and widely distributed, it makes a good **zone fossil**. To correlate strata on a regional basis the stratigrapher will establish both the sequence of rock layers and the distribution of fossils within those layers. This work will initially be undertaken at the best locality within the area, where the rocks would ideally be undisturbed and represent the thickest sequence. Having recorded the variation in thicknesses and rock type and the occurrence of fossils, the stratigrapher would then be equipped to correlate with outcrops elsewhere within the area. For example, if he moves to an area with the same fossil content he can infer that the sequence is once more undisturbed. If however the fossils occur in the reverse order he can recognise that the sequence is overturned. He will also be able to see if specific fossils are absent in some outcrops and deduce either a change in environmental conditions or the non-deposition of strata.

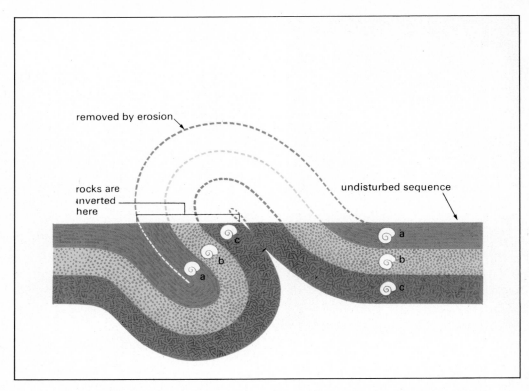

The succession of fossils within the stratigraphic column is also evidence for the course of evolution. It is obvious to most scientists that geological time has witnessed major changes in the earth's animal and plant life, and an accurate documentation of events indicates that more advanced or better adapted organisms have appeared at frequent intervals during the last 2 billion years.

When surveying the strata of an area a geologist first needs to study an undisturbed section of rock in order to assess the correct sequence of rocks and their associated zone fossils. This will enable him to discover whether the rocks in adjacent areas have been folded or not.

The relationships of the flora and fauna to their aquatic habitats. A, the basic subdivisions of both marine and terrestrial environments; B, the distribution of algae and invertebrate animals (both past and present) in aquatic environments.

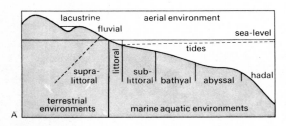

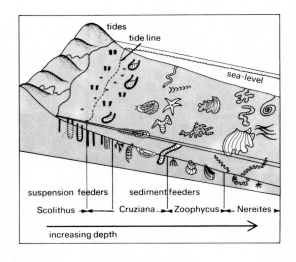

Trace fossils are very useful for the recognition of environments throughout the stratigraphic column, and their complexity often reflects the feeding habits of the animal involved in their construction.

This chart shows the history of life. It also divides geological time into the main periods and eras. To illustrate the life of a single human on the chart is impossible.

Eras	Invertebrate and Plant Life	Vertebrate Life

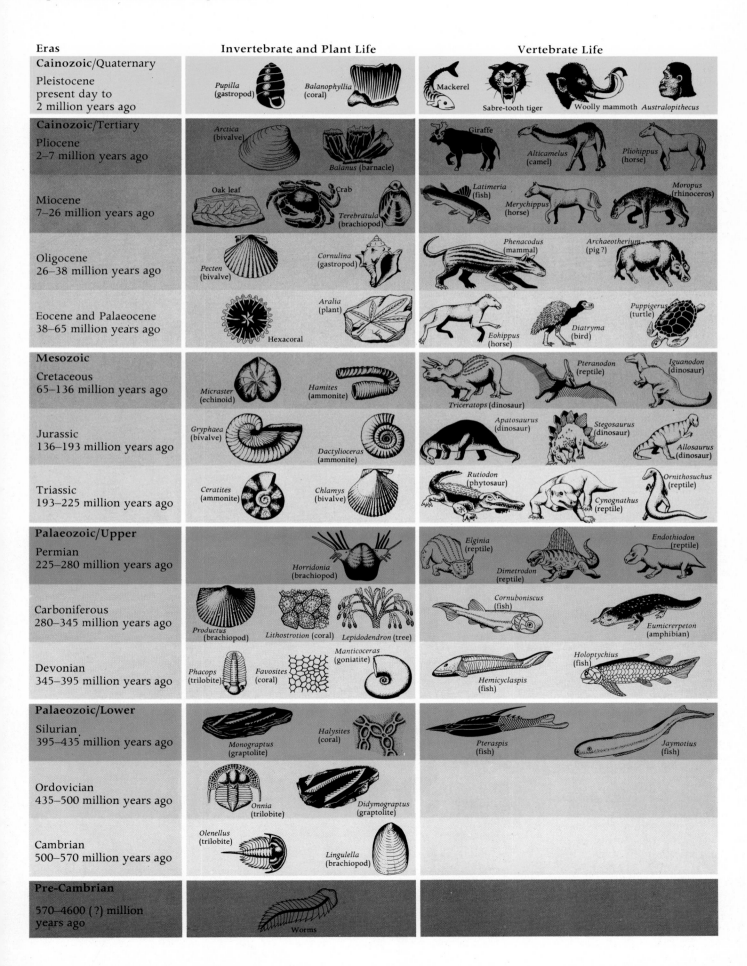

Cainozoic/Quaternary
Pleistocene
present day to
2 million years ago

Pupilla (gastropod) *Balanophyllia* (coral)

Mackerel Sabre-tooth tiger Woolly mammoth *Australopithecus*

Cainozoic/Tertiary
Pliocene
2–7 million years ago

Arctica (bivalve) *Balanus* (barnacle)

Giraffe *Alticamelus* (camel) *Pliohippus* (horse)

Miocene
7–26 million years ago

Oak leaf Crab *Terebratula* (brachiopod)

Latimeria (fish) *Merychippus* (horse) *Moropus* (rhinoceros)

Oligocene
26–38 million years ago

Pecten (bivalve) *Cornulina* (gastropod)

Phenacodus (mammal) *Archaeotherium* (pig?)

Eocene and Palaeocene
38–65 million years ago

Aralia (plant) Hexacoral

Eohippus (horse) *Diatryma* (bird) *Puppigerus* (turtle)

Mesozoic
Cretaceous
65–136 million years ago

Micraster (echinoid) *Hamites* (ammonite)

Triceratops (dinosaur) *Pteranodon* (reptile) *Iguanodon* (dinosaur)

Jurassic
136–193 million years ago

Gryphaea (bivalve) *Dactylioceras* (ammonite)

Apatosaurus (dinosaur) *Stegosaurus* (dinosaur) *Allosaurus* (dinosaur)

Triassic
193–225 million years ago

Ceratites (ammonite) *Chlamys* (bivalve)

Rutiodon (phytosaur) *Cynognathus* (reptile) *Ornithosuchus* (reptile)

Palaeozoic/Upper
Permian
225–280 million years ago

Horridonia (brachiopod)

Elginia (reptile) *Dimetrodon* (reptile) *Endothiodon* (reptile)

Carboniferous
280–345 million years ago

Productus (brachiopod) *Lithostrotion* (coral) *Lepidodendron* (tree)

Cornuboniscus (fish) *Eumicrerpeton* (amphibian)

Devonian
345–395 million years ago

Phacops (trilobite) *Favosites* (coral) *Manticoceras* (goniatite)

Hemicyclaspis (fish) *Holoptychius* (fish)

Palaeozoic/Lower
Silurian
395–435 million years ago

Monograptus (graptolite) *Halysites* (coral)

Pteraspis (fish) *Jaymotius* (fish)

Ordovician
435–500 million years ago

Onnia (trilobite) *Didymograptus* (graptolite)

Cambrian
500–570 million years ago

Olenellus (trilobite) *Lingulella* (brachiopod)

Pre-Cambrian
570–4600 (?) million years ago

Worms

Collecting and preparation

History's great palaeontologists were dedicated collectors and field workers and our museum collections and galleries bear testimony to their enterprise. The collections of Edward Drinker Cope (1840–97) and Othniel Charles Marsh (1831–99) are among the more spectacular but the history of palaeontology is interwoven with tales of interesting discoveries and major expeditions. Amateur geologists have also played an important role and the work of Mary Anning (1799–1847) is known to most enthusiasts. Born in Lyme Regis, Mary became an ardent collector and from the age of 11 recorded some of the most important finds in vertebrate palaeontology. In those days the collection and preparation of a specimen relied on intensive labour. Men would carefully lift the block containing the specimen from the quarry or cliff and transport it to a workshop where they would use hammers, mallets and chisels of all sizes to remove the sediment. They were craftsmen and the delicate skills they brought to the job enabled equally skilled scientists to measure and describe the fossils in great detail.

Today, palaeontologists still take meticulous care with the collection, preparation and curation of material. The collection of fossils demands the same attention to detail, whether during a major expedition to Antarctica or on a visit to a local quarry. The correct equipment is essential and a notebook and camera are just as important as a hammer. On site, one should first record in a field notebook the extent of an outcrop and the nature of the rock types along with notes on the positions and relationships of any fossils. Measurements should also be logged, along with any facts that will be relevant for any reconstruction.

The collection of fossils can often be done from loose blocks or scree slopes, but specimens on the rock face are often best left undisturbed. They may be damaged by poor collecting techniques but when left can be studied by many other geologists. The removal of a specimen requires care and attention to detail. Aimless hammering will ruin both the specimen and the outcrop and possibly result in serious injury. Skilled collectors work well away from the specimen and apply a paper and plaster jacket to their more delicate finds. They never try to prepare the specimen under field conditions.

In the laboratory, the specimens can first be curated and then prepared. Curation involves the assigning of a reference number and the positioning of the specimen within the relevant stratigraphical, regional or systematic collection. All the details of site, geological horizon and age are recorded diligently. Hammers, small chisels and strong pins are still used during preparation, but air abrasive or air dent equipment is now included in

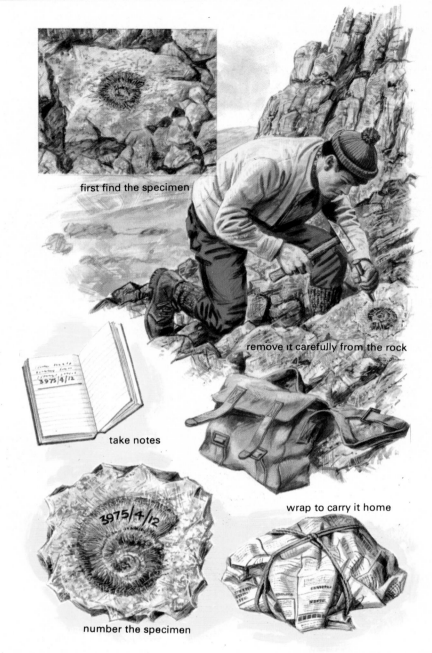

first find the specimen

remove it carefully from the rock

take notes

wrap to carry it home

number the specimen

Above: **Palaeontologists need to be well equipped to collect, label and transport new discoveries. Undocumented specimens are of little value.**

Below: **The Blue Lias rocks of Lyme Regis, England are rich in Mesozoic fossils, and it was here that Mary Anning, then 11, discovered the skeleton of an *Ichthyosaurus*.**

most laboratories since they can clean the inside of the fossil as well as the outside and can reveal the finest details of ornament and structure. Chemical techniques are also used in most major laboratories and acids have become the most important 'tools' in the preparation of certain fossils including graptolites and vertebrates. The use of acids is a specialist job.

It is dangerous and the wrong approach will invariably ruin the specimen. In a museum laboratory the preparation of a large vertebrate fossil may take months or years. The acids used include acetic and hydrochloric acid but their strength rarely exceeds a 10% concentration. After a few hours in acid, the specimen is washed carefully in deionised water,

dried and the newly exposed areas of bone coated with a plastic-based glue. When this is dry the procedure is repeated, and after preparation the specimen is stored and exhibited.

The use of Plaster of Paris and bandages is important for the safe removal and transportation of large fossils.

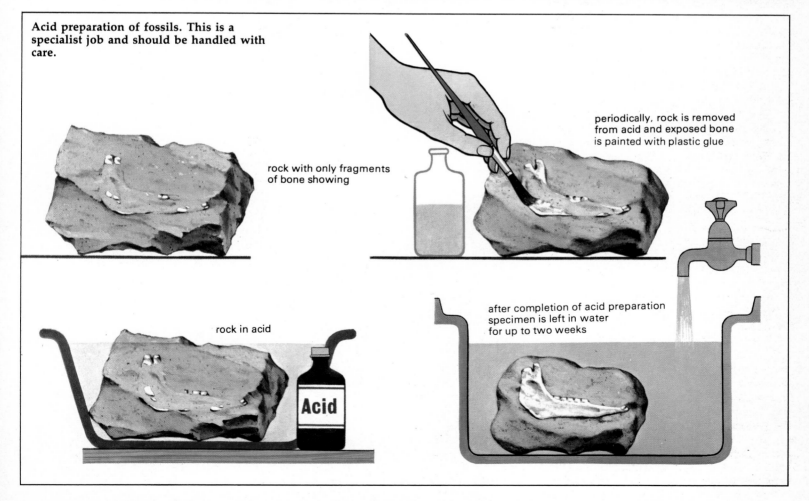

Acid preparation of fossils. This is a specialist job and should be handled with care.

rock with only fragments of bone showing

periodically, rock is removed from acid and exposed bone is painted with plastic glue

rock in acid

Acid

after completion of acid preparation specimen is left in water for up to two weeks

Great palaeontologists and naturalists

Men have been interested in fossils for hundreds of years, but until the 17th century they were considered to be merely 'outgrowths from the earth' or 'sports of nature'. By the 16th century Conrad Gesner (1516–65) had illustrated fossils in his text *De Rerum Fossilium* and beautiful illustrations became common in the 17th and 18th centuries. Buffon (1707–88) wrote on the succession of animals and plants, and William Smith (1769–1839) discussed the use of fossils in the identification of geological strata.

Baron Georges Cuvier (1769–1832), an outstanding French naturalist, compared the anatomy of living and fossil organisms and laid the foundations of vertebrate palaeontology. However, although he and his contemporaries realised what fossils were, they did not comprehend the idea of evolution, but thought of fossils as being the remains of animals that existed before Man and were destroyed in a series of catastrophes of which the Biblical Flood was the last. In contrast, Jean Baptiste Lamarck (1744–1829) believed in the inheritance of acquired characters and in the importance of environmental pressures. A simple illustration of his views is that of successive generations of giraffes straining to eat leaves just out of reach and so developing longer and longer necks. Great palaeontologists such as Sir Richard Owen (1804–92) and William Buckland (1784–1856) would have no truck with evolution, which had been propounded by Charles Darwin (1809–82) and Alfred Wallace (1823–1914), and in which fossils played an important part.

The 19th century saw the birth of public interest in geology and palaeontology. The first descriptions of dinosaurs were published in quick succession by Buckland in 1824 and in 1825 by Gideon Mantell (1790–1852). The 'terrible-lizards' captured the minds of the populace and gigantic reconstructions of *Iguanodon* and *Megalosaurus*, conceived by Owen, were modelled in 1854 and still dominate the grounds of Crystal Palace, London. Dinosaur hunting developed to a fever pitch. North America became the centre of interest and Edward Drinker Cope (1840–97) and Othniel Charles Marsh (1831–99), who were motivated by an extreme dislike for each other, collected hundreds of tons of dinosaur bones. Dinosaur, a town in Colorado with street names such as Stegosaurus Freeway, is the administrative centre of the Dinosaur National Monument. The area was designated a national monument by President Woodrow Wilson to protect the excavation areas from possible development.

Great palaeontologists were not confined to the 19th century. Edward Suess (1831–1914) was still active at the end of his life. His interest in a possible land bridge between Africa and southern Europe remains pertinent today in terms of palaeography and the distribution of faunas. Louis Dollo (1857–1931) wrote hundreds of scientific papers on vertebrate fossils, among which were a number of papers on the ornithischian dinosaur *Iguanodon*. The 31 animals described by Dollo from the Cretaceous Period of Bernissart in Belgium can be seen today in the Institut Royal, Brussels. During the 20th century, the emphasis within vertebrate palaeontology has moved towards fossil man. Raymond Dart and Louis Leakey (1903–72) stand out in this field but others who are very young by comparison have already made significant contributions to this science.

William Buckland

The evolution of the giraffe provided the classic example for Lamarck's theories on the 'inheritance of acquired characters'.

Jean Baptiste Lamark

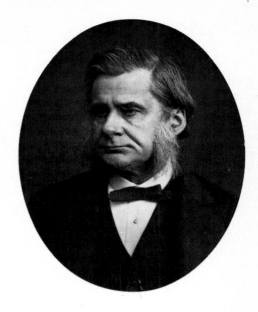

Charles Darwin *(left)*, Thomas Huxley *(above)* and Sir Richard Owen *(below)* were amongst the most important scientists of the 19th century. Of the three, only Owen disbelieved the theory of evolution.
Bottom: A skeleton of an *Iguanodon,* one of the first dinosaurs to be identified.

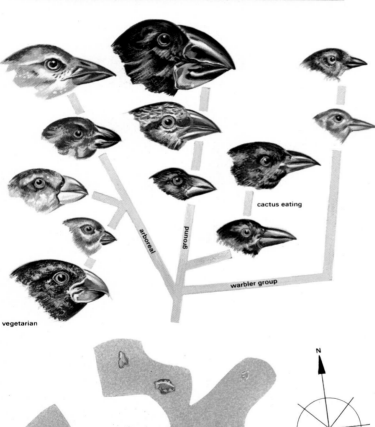

cactus eating

arboreal

ground

warbler group

vegetarian

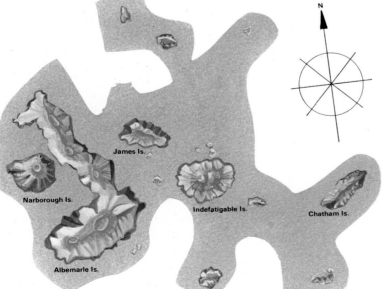

James Is.

Narborough Is.

Indefatigable Is.

Chatham Is.

Albemarle Is.

The range of bill shapes amongst the isolated finches of the Galapagos islands provided Darwin with important evidence for his theory of evolution while on his historic voyage on the H.M.S. Beagle.

Evolution

The word 'evolution' means to unfold, and it is used by scientists to explain the process of change by which living species have descended from ancient ancestors. Evolution is a relatively new concept and we should remember that little over a hundred years have passed since Darwin's ideas on the 'survival of the fittest' and of natural selection were first accepted. Before Darwin most palaeon-tologists and naturalists believed in the Great Flood theory, with successive groups of fossils accumulating as a result of sudden catastrophies. Only Jean Baptiste Lamarck challenged the accepted principles of the day, but his ideas about the inheritance of parental characteristics by offspring received scant reward.

Darwin realised that competition amongst animals resulted in those best suited to cope with change and challenge persisting. Variations in living conditions that reduced the effectiveness of a species would eventually result in its de-mise and extinction. He did not fully un-derstand the mechanisms of evolution or inheritance and it was left to the botanist Gregor Mendel (1822–84), to lay the foun-dations of genetics through a series of breeding experiments. Since Mendel, a great deal of work has been done on gen-etics and on the structure and composi-tion of cells. The mechanisms of inheritance are constantly being investi-gated and the construction of genetic or 'linkage' maps is an accepted practice. However, some modern palaeontologists believe that the importance of fossils to our understanding of evolution is lim-ited, because they contend that family trees based on fossil evidence cannot be tested scientifically; some even support more sophisticated variations of the creationist-catastrophist line of pre-Dar-winian science.

Left above: **Greek philosophers such as Aristotle thought that life began as undifferentiated 'matter' with a 'potentiality' for turning into a form which could change by stages, such as a hen's egg into a chicken.**

Left below: **Mendel conducted many experiments which showed how various characteristics could be inherited. This illustration shows the results of one of his experiments using seed form and colour as contrasting characteristics. Here the second filial generation showed four different combined sets of characters.**

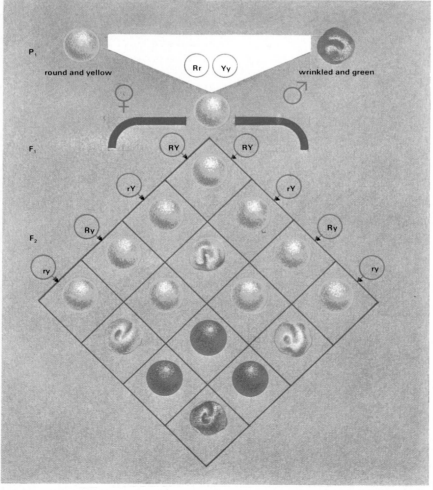

Colour variations in the bivalve *Chlamys varia* (variegated scallop). If any variant was better suited to the environment, it would be favoured through natural selection.

Classification

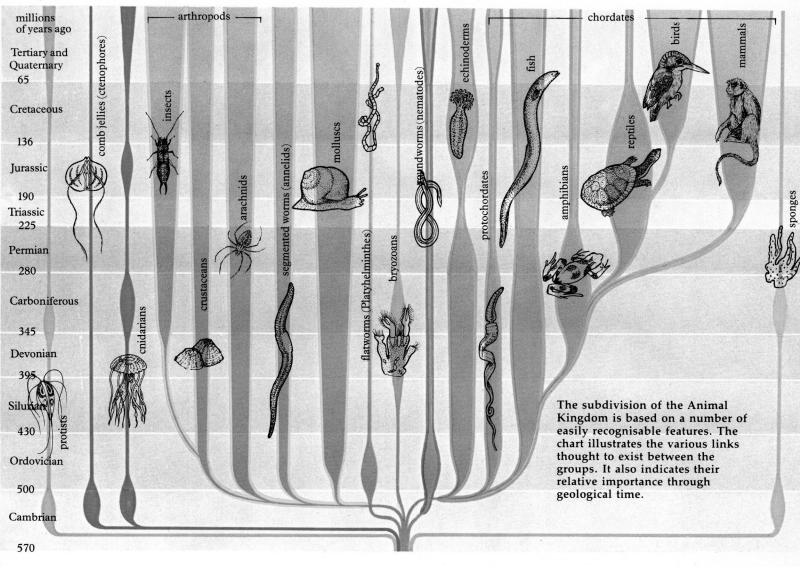

millions of years ago

Tertiary and Quaternary 65

Cretaceous

136

Jurassic

190

Triassic 225

Permian

280

Carboniferous

345

Devonian

395

Silurian

430

Ordovician

500

Cambrian

570

period

comb jellies (ctenophores)

arthropods

insects

arachnids

crustaceans

cnidarians

protists

segmented worms (annelids)

molluscs

flatworms (Platyhelminthes)

bryozoans

roundworms (nematodes)

echinoderms

protochordates

fish

amphibians

reptiles

chordates

birds

mammals

sponges

The subdivision of the Animal Kingdom is based on a number of easily recognisable features. The chart illustrates the various links thought to exist between the groups. It also indicates their relative importance through geological time.

Classification is the grouping of animals and plants according to their similarities. The largest groups or *taxa* are the Plant and Animal Kingdoms which are then subdivided into *phyla* (singular – *phylum*). Each phylum is based on one or more fundamental characters: all chordates, for example, have an internal rod or notochord at some time in their development and this is a shared link between the lowly *Amphioxus* and Man himself. The fishes, amphibians, reptiles and mammals are *classes* of chordates, each with its own taxonomic criteria. Classes are made up of *orders* and *sub-orders* whose members have more obvious similarities. And again, orders may be further divided into families, and sub-divided yet again into various *genera* (singular – *genus*). A *genus* is formed of a number of associated *species* which are isolated from each other because they cannot interbreed successfully. For example, *Canis* is the scientific name of the dog genus and *Canis familiaris* (domestic dog), *Canis lupus* (wolf), *Canis latrans* (coyote) and *Canis mesomelas* (black-backed jackal) are representative species.

Animals such as the vertebrates radiate into a variety of forms, and a series of names are given to the differently sized groups.

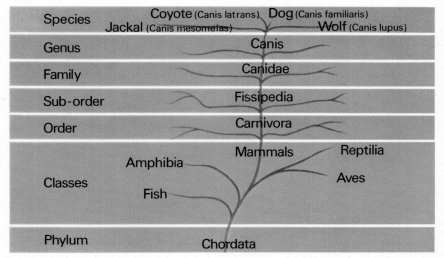

Species	Coyote (*Canis latrans*) Dog (*Canis familiaris*) Jackal (*Canis mesomelas*) Wolf (*Canis lupus*)
Genus	Canis
Family	Canidae
Sub-order	Fissipedia
Order	Carnivora
Classes	Amphibia Fish Mammals Reptilia Aves
Phylum	Chordata

The generic name is the first of the two latinised names attributed to every animal or plant; the second is the specific name. This binomial system, which was begun by Carolus Linnaeus (1707–78), has succeeded in eliminating many of the problems of duplicate names and when used correctly can provide some information on the kind of organism one is dealing with. For instance, *Tyrannosaurus rex* is without doubt the 'King of the tyrant-lizards'.

Classification

A study of both the fossil record and the present day animal and plant kingdoms reveals a truly staggering diversity in form. To simply name these organisms would generate a multitude of names which would serve no useful purpose and create confusion. Biologists and paleontologists overcome this problem by grouping certain organisms together on the basis of morphological similarity. This sorting of organisms of similar appearance is termed classification *and provides an ordered system for categorising animals and plants.*

The theory and practice of classification is called taxonomy. *Two new approaches to taxonomy are currently in vogue, namely* cladistics *and* numerical taxonomy. *Cladistics depends on morphological structure and the presence of what are deemed to be shared, uniquely derived characters, resulting in a classification that supposedly accurately reflects the evolutionary processes that are thought to have occurred. Numerical taxonomy relies on computerised techniques, with numerical counts and measurements of observable characters being employed. Both approaches are controversial and neither have gained complete acceptance from taxonomists.*

Early plants

The first organisms to appear on this planet were single-celled organisms with a loosely organised nucleus. They are termed procaryotes and living representatives include the blue-green algae and bacteria. These first occurred approximately 3000 million years ago in the Precambrian. The blue-green algae exist as single units or in strands, and are capable of photosynthesis, which played an important part in the development of an oxygen-rich atmosphere. Sediment-accreting, blue-green algae can be recognised by the banded or ring-like structure of their colonies, known as stromatolites. More advanced types of algae appeared in the late Precambrian and early Cambrian and probably the seaweeds were an important part of marine floras over 600 million years ago.

Terrestrial plants first appeared in the Silurian Period. The earliest true land plant is *Cooksonia*, a delicate, dichotomously (equal) branching genus which carried its reproductive sporangia at the tips of its branches. It was an erect plant with an underground rooting structure known as the rhizome. *Cooksonia* was the precursor of all land plants and a close relative of the living *Psilotum* and *Tmesipteris*.

During the early Devonian, the psilopsids and primitive lycopsids such as *Psilophyton* and *Asteroxylon* thrived along river banks and in swamps. *Asteroxylon* and also *Drepanophycus* were characterised by short, tightly packed leaflets. By the Upper Devonian, early representatives of the horsetails, seed ferns and cordaitaleans (ancestral conifers) had appeared, and a great diversification of non-flowering plants took place in the Carboniferous, with great forests of horsetails (*Calamites*) and scale trees (*Lepidodendron*) covering many regions. Their success was due to modifications in their reproductive habits and enhanced protection of the spore or seed. The development of the protected seed is regarded by some scientists as being as important in plants as the development of the amniote egg in reptiles. Non-flowering plants in the form of ferns, bennettitaleans, cycads, gingkos and conifers dominated world floras until the Cretaceous and the expansion of the flowering plants, or angiosperms.

The ferns, horsetails and club mosses inherited the primitive reproductive habits of their psilopsid ancestors. Terminal sporangia persisted in *Zosterophyllum* and *Horneophyton*: it is essential that their reproductive cycle is carried out in water. In contrast, the living club-moss *Selaginella* has small cone-like structures in which the spores are protected by small leaflets. Such an advance allowed these early plants to migrate into new habitats. Cone-like reproductive organs are recorded amongst Carboniferous plants.

Certain fern genera bore their sporangia on the underside of the leaf. This development is a major advance over the primitive condition but is itself limiting. 'Naked seed' plants began to dominate world floras in the Carboniferous, and represent a significant step in the conquest of dry land. In such plants, the male and female reproductive cells are borne in separate cones and 'pollination' is essential for fertilization to occur. Advanced conifers protect their eggs inside the individual scales of a woody cone, while the male seeds or pollen are borne on smaller cones. In primitive plants, the microspores had to 'swim' to fertilize the main cell, whereas in conifers the microspores or pollen are carried by the wind. An overproduction of pollen

Tightly packed fossil stromatolites closely resemble the blue-green algal colonies found today in Sharks Bay, Australia.

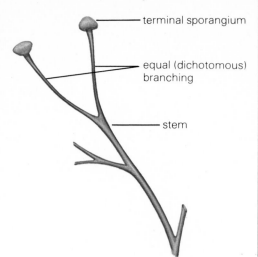

terminal sporangium

equal (dichotomous) branching

stem

A reconstruction of the primitive land-dwelling psilopsid *Cooksonia*.

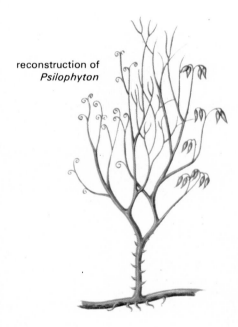

reconstruction of *Psilophyton*

A reconstruction of *Psilophyton*, an early Devonian plant.

A reconstruction of *Drepanophycus*, an early Devonian plant showing a more complex structure than *Cooksonia*.

Tertiary and Quaternary

65

Cretaceous

136

Jurassic

190

Triassic

225

Permian

280

Carboniferous

345

Devonian

395

millions of years ago

cycads

ginkgos

conifers

flowering plants

ferns

Bennettitales

horsetails

lycopods

seed ferns

Cordaitales

the primitives

Land plants first appeared in the Upper Silurian. Various evolutionary changes have culminated in the development of the protected seed and of brightly coloured flowers. The evolution of the plants in terms of their structure, reproduction and distribution is comparable with that of the Animal Kingdom.

23

Early plants (continued)

grains increases the chance that at least one reaches the inside of the female cone where it develops a pollen tube and fertilizes the egg. The development of this sequence of reproductive and distributive features aided gymnosperm evolution. During the Upper Palaeozoic, the conifers underwent considerable radiation and several major geographic groupings can be identified. The gingkos also appeared in the Upper Carboniferous-Early Permian and it is likely that they shared the same cordaitalean ancestors as the conifers. Successive radiations of 'naked seed' plants occurred throughout the Mesozoic.

In the Cretaceous, the flowering plants became common with their seeds 'double wrapped' for protection. Angiosperm means 'enclosed seed' and the advanced features of the group include the development of a flower with a receptive stigma, double fertilization, the enclosure of the reproductive apparatus inside the ovary, and a fruit surrounding the seed to encourage distribution by animals as well as by wind and water. The pollen for fertilization is also transported by many mechanisms, with the flower encouraging bees and other insects to act as pollinators. Cross-fertilization is the result: it ensures that genetic information is transferred within a species more efficiently.

Two modern representatives of the primitive plant group: Thallophyta.

Fossil *Chara*, a member of one of the simplest plant groups – the algae. These algae represent a distinct evolutionary line away from the blue-green algae, reproducing sexually.

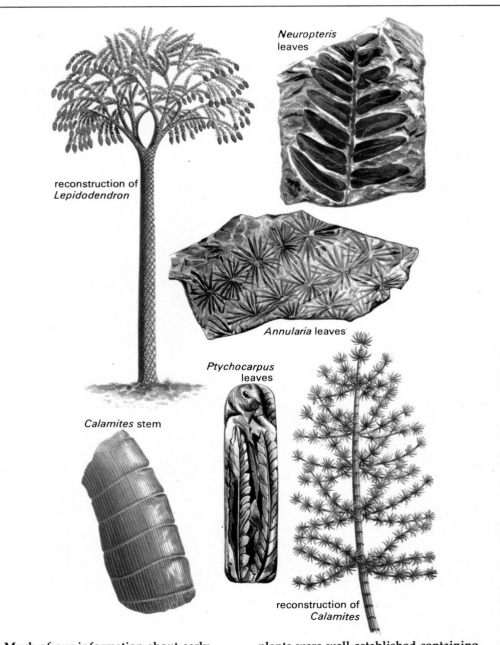

Much of our information about early plants comes from study of the huge fossil floras known from the coal measures of the world. By the Carboniferous, land plants were well established containing many forms such as the scale tree, *Lepidodendron* and the ancient tree fern, *Calamites*.

Life-cycle of a typical gymnosperm – the Scots pine *Pinus sylvestris*.

The variety of leaf shape is greater among flowering plants than among gymnosperms. Their vascular tissues are also unique and can be linked with the successful adaptation of the group to seasonal climatic conditions. The drifting of the continents during the Cretaceous was accompanied by an increased seasonality, and this coincided with the worldwide expansion of the angiosperms. Leaf beds and the remains of fossil angiosperm woods are common in Tertiary strata.

Below: **a fossilized piece of *Lepidodendron* showing the dense covering of leaf scars on the trunk.** *Middle:* **A cone of *Araucaria* (monkey-puzzle trees) from the Cretaceous.** *Bottom:* **A fossilized leaf of the *Ginkgo* from the Jurassic. This tree can still be found today.**

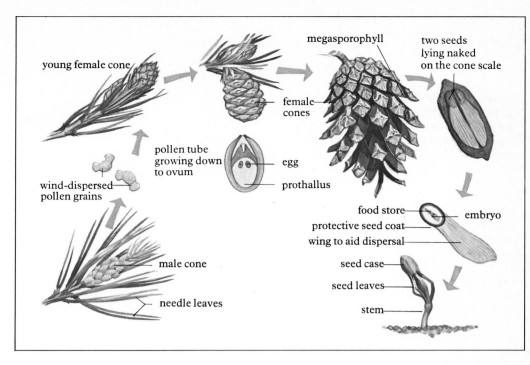

piece of *Lepidodendron* showing leaf scars

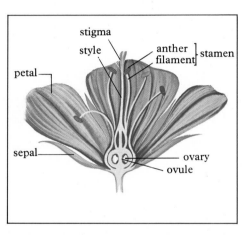

Vertical section through a flower to show the basic parts.

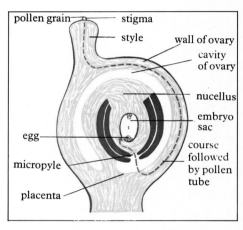

Vertical section through an angiosperm carpel showing events following pollination, leading to fertilization.

cone *Araucaria* Cretaceous

Some typical fruits and seeds from members of the highly successful angiosperms.

Below: **A fossilized oak leaf (*Quercus*) from the Pleistocene.**

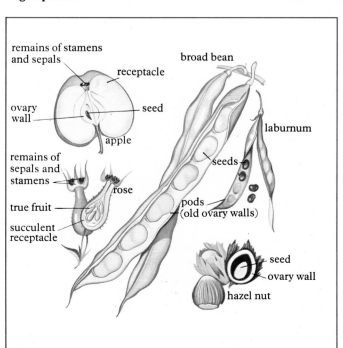

Ginkgo
leaf Jurassic   Recent

oak leaf Pleistocene

Invertebrates

Protozoans – Sponges – Corals

Invertebrates are all the animals that have no backbone, although they may still have complex bodies. The first animals were invertebrates and appeared in the Precambrian Period. They were probably single-celled protozoans similar to the living *Amoeba*. From these, individual animals with protective envelopes developed followed by others with calcareous and siliceous tests. In time these external skeletons became more complex with many chambers and various patterns of coiling. Many protozoans are microscopic but large forms such as the nummulites, fusulinids and alveolinids appear at various times in the stratigraphic record; all three groups are useful to the stratigrapher. Protozoans are adapted to many ecological niches and are useful indicators of the environment.

Numerous other families of organisms which lacked exoskeletons also evolved. It is possible that individuals of different shapes and modes of life linked to perform functions of mutual benefit. This may have led to the development of the

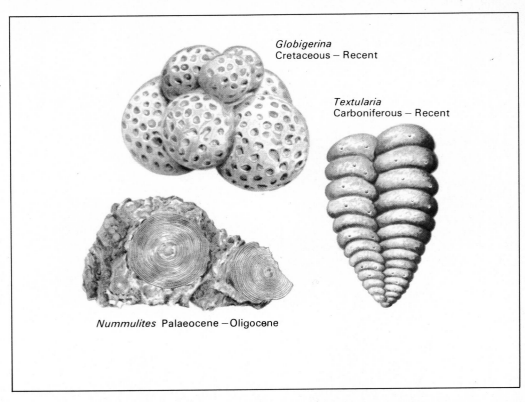

Globigerina
Cretaceous – Recent

Textularia
Carboniferous – Recent

Nummulites Palaeocene – Oligocene

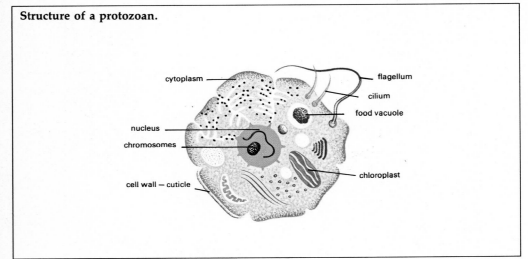

Structure of a protozoan.

cytoplasm · flagellum · cilium · food vacuole · nucleus · chromosomes · chloroplast · cell wall – cuticle

Above: **Foraminiferids (marine protozoans) are useful zone fossils:** *Globigerina* **is planktonic, the others lived on the sea floor.**

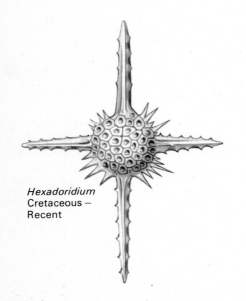

Hexadoridium
Cretaceous –
Recent

Hexadoridium is a radiolarian protozoan that swims near the surface of the sea.

first 'multicellular' organism and triggered the development of advanced animals.

The first many-celled animals were the sponges, which began in the Precambrian. These have no mouth or anus and their cells do not form distinct tissues. Sponges have either siliceous or calcareous skeletons which are made up of variously shaped spicules. They are fairly good indicators of depth and environment. The numerous pores which pierce the soft tissues of the sponge allow for the passage of water rich in oxygen and food. Similar pore structures occur in the exclusively Cambrian archaeocyathids, but these animals have a complex double wall structure and horizontal and vertical plates which separate them from the simpler sponges.

It is possible that the archaeocyathids have closer links with the coelenterates, but such an evolutionary tie is difficult to establish. The coelenterates, in the form

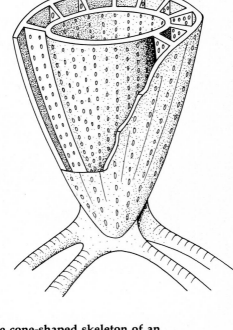

The cone-shaped skeleton of an archaeocyathid is different from that of any other known organism. It consists of coarse calcareous needles and the walls are connected by horizontal and vertical partitions which resemble similar structures in the stony corals. The actual animals probably lived between the walls.

of jellyfishes and hydrozoans, first appear in the Precambrian, and forms similar to the Portuguese Man-o'-War jellyfish are recorded from rocks 600 million years old.

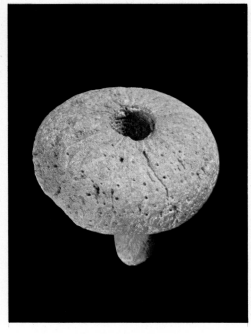

Siphonia, a member of the siliceous demosponges, found from the middle Cretaceous to the Tertiary.

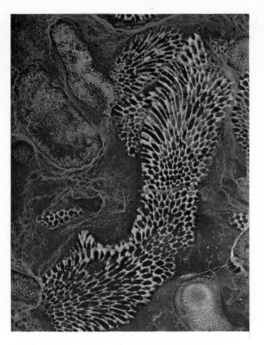

Thamnopora, a member of the tabulate corals, these were colonial animals with individual skeletons. This genus was found worldwide from the Silurian to the Permian.

Acervularia, a rugose coral forming massive colonies in which the individual units (corallites) are closely united and polygonal in shape. This genus is from the Silurian.

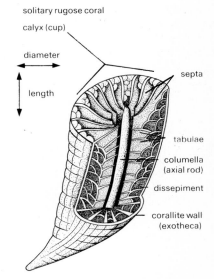

A solitary rugose coral showing the internal structure.

Left: The archaeocyathids superficially resemble the rugose corals *(above)*. The two are quite different however, and the coral skeleton is much more complex.

The stony corals first appeared in the Ordovician. During the Palaeozoic Era, various species of tabulate and rugose coral flourished in warm tropical and subtropical areas. The tabulates were exclusively colonial and genera such as *Favosites* and *Syringopora* were abundant in Silurian and Devonian reef communities. Amongst the rugose corals solitary and colonial species are common from the late Ordovician onwards. During the Carboniferous Period, rugose corals including *Lonsdaleia*, *Dibunophyllum* and *Caninia* are used as stratigraphic indicators. Both the tabulate and rugose corals died out at the end of the Palaeozoic and were replaced in the Mesozoic Era by the scleractinians which still contribute to the building of reefs.

Invertebrates

Worms, Bryozoans and Brachiopods

In contrast to the simple structure of the sponges or the two-layered nature of the corals and related groups, the primitive platyhelminth worms have three layers of tissues in their body wall. Unlike the annelid worms, the platyhelminths are unsegmented. In the annelids, other invertebrates, and the vertebrates, the middle layer or mesoderm forms a fluid-filled cavity called the coelom. In the worms, the coelom functions as a hydrostatic skeleton, whilst in the more advanced animals it stores internal organs and vital materials. The worms first appeared in the Precambrian and their traces are found throughout the geological record.

Numerous groups are thought to have had a worm-like ancestor including the important minor coelomates: the bryozoans and the brachiopods. It is difficult at first to understand the link between them, although both groups possess a coelom and both have a tentacular feeding organ called the lophophore.

The bryozoans are tiny colonial organisms which first appear in the Ordovician and are known from 18500 living and fos-

Fenestella, a member of the 'lace bryozoans'. The colony consists of numerous parallel branches connected at intervals by thin crossbars. These were very common in the Upper Palaeozoic.

sil species. The bryozoan skeleton consists of hundreds of small boxes arranged along branches or over the surface of globular structures. Lace-like bryozoans such as *Fenestella* are amongst the most exquisite fossils found in Palaeozoic communities.

The brachiopods first appeared in the Lower Cambrian and belonged to the 'inarticulate' class of brachiopods that are characterised by the lack of an internal lophophore support and the absence of dentition inside a non-calcareous shell. *Lingulella* from the Cambro-Ordovician is a typical inarticulate, and is very similar to its living relative *Lingula*. The 'articulate' brachiopods also first appear in the Cambrian. They have calcareous shells and may develop a well-formed internal support for the lophophore. Two-valved brachiopods flourished during the Palaeozoic in various environments: the best known include *Spirifer*, *Productus* and *Terebratula*. In the Mesozoic the brachiopods are more limited for many niches were filled by the rapidly evolving bivalves.

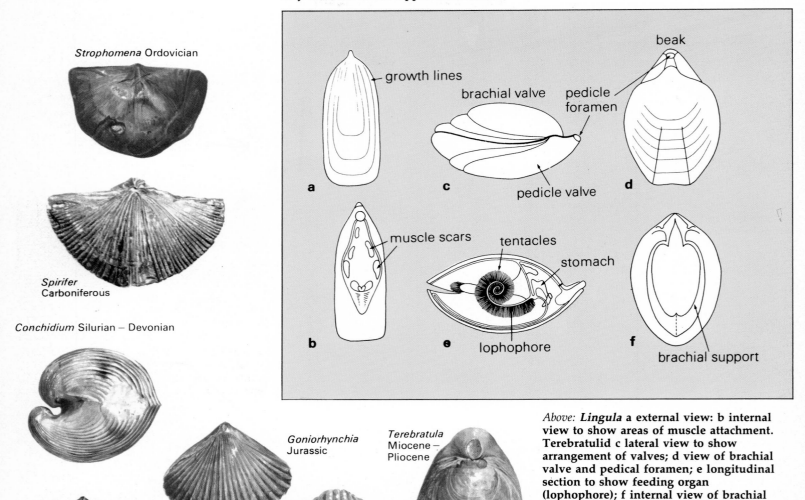

Strophomena Ordovician

Spirifer Carboniferous

Conchidium Silurian – Devonian

Orthis Cambrian – Ordovician

Goniorhynchia Jurassic

Dielasma Carboniferous – Permian

Terebratula Miocene – Pliocene

Above: **Lingula a external view: b internal view to show areas of muscle attachment. Terebratulid c lateral view to show arrangement of valves; d view of brachial valve and pedical foramen; e longitudinal section to show feeding organ (lophophore); f internal view of brachial valve showing support structure.**

Left: **Six brachiopods. They are important fossils, and over 30 000 species are recognised.**

28

Mollusca – bivalves

The bivalves are part of the phylum Mollusca and as such are relatives of animals as diverse as slugs and snails (gastropods), plated chitons, elongate scaphopods, the squids, cuttlefish, octupuses, as well as the nautiloids and the extinct ammonoids and belemnites. Molluscs are essentially marine animals, although bivalves and gastropods do occupy freshwater niches. Only the gastropods have adapted to a terrestrial mode of life.

The bivalves first appeared in the early Ordovician, and although their two-valved shell has restricted their evolution they have been extremely successful since the beginning of the Triassic. This may coincide with the perfection of elongate siphons which help in the processes of feeding and respiration. Siphons are of particular value in a burrowing mode of life and are not present in free-living, swimming or fixed varieties. Shell form and dentition is important in the classification of fossil bivalves. Oysters (fixed), cockles (shallow burrowers), mussels (attached), scallops (free-swimming) are examples of successful bivalve stocks.

Plagiostoma, a medium-to large-sized bivalve mollusc; it is relatively abundant in the shallow-water limestones of the Lower Jurassic.

Nucula, a shallow burrowing bivalve mollusc. Its rounded shell differs from the more elongated forms of the deeper-burrowing types.

Bivalves. a view of bivalve with left valve removed; **b** *Arca,* taxodont dentition, equal muscle scars; **c** *Pecten,* dysodont dentition, single muscle scar; **d** *Venericor,* heterodont dentition, unequal muscle scars; **e** *Venericor,* external view of valve to show growth lines and longitudinal ornament.

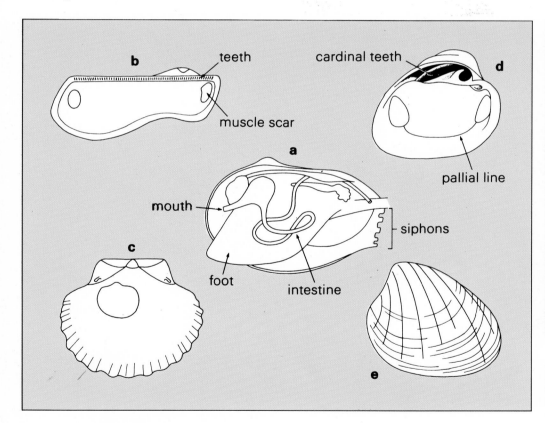

Lithophaga, unlike the majority of bivalves, is a borer, excavating a cylindrical burrow in a rock by means of a chemical solution.

Clams, chitons, snails and octopi are living representatives of the Mollusca. Of these only the snails have evolved to occupy land-dwelling niches.

Invertebrates

Mollusca – gastropods

Of the other mollusc groups, the gastropods first appeared in the early Cambrian. Unlike the bivalves they have a single, coiled shell, and the body is elongate with a well-defined head and a large muscular foot. Some gastropods have lungs but the majority possess gills. They feed by using a rasping jaw, the radula; different animals have adapted to carnivorous, herbivorous or coprophilic (faeces-ingesting) feeding modes. During the Palaeozoic, planispirally coiled forms were common (*Planorbis* is a later example). Later, high spired forms became more abundant. Active predators such as *Natica* and planktonic forms (pteropods etc.) are also important in the Cainozoic.

Mollusca – cephalopods

The most advanced class of molluscs are the cephalopods. These are now represented by the living *Nautilus*, the argonauts, cuttlefish, octopuses and squids. The cephalopods have a well-developed head with large eyes and a well-formed brain. They first appeared in the Ordovician with ancient relatives of the *Nautilus* as the first representatives of the class. These early nautiloids had a variety of shell shapes and several types of mineral deposits within the shell chambers to stabilise the position of these marine animals whilst they fed or moved. Several species of straight-shelled nautiloid grew several metres long.

A second major group of cephalopods, the ammonoids, arose from the straight-shelled bactritoids in the early Devonian. The earliest ammonoids, known as goniatites, had a rather simple structure which becomes more complex in the ceratites and the Mesozoic ammonite stocks. The goniatites are used as zone fossils in the Upper Palaeozoic. By the Triassic, they had been replaced by the ceratites which in turn were replaced by the ammonites in the Jurassic of which *Phylloceras* is an example. Ammonites are abundant in Jurassic and Cretaceous strata and short-lived, cosmopolitan species are ideal zone fossils.

The ammonites flourished in the warm lime-rich seas of the Tethyan region. In

Structure of a gastropod

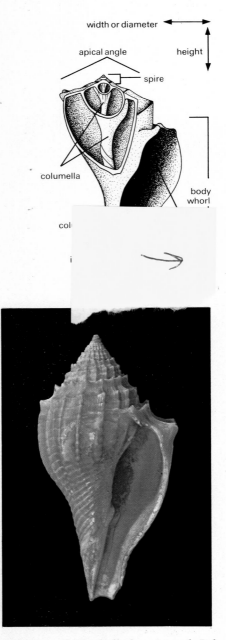

Athleta, a thick-shelled gastropod. It has a short spine and turban-like protoconch.

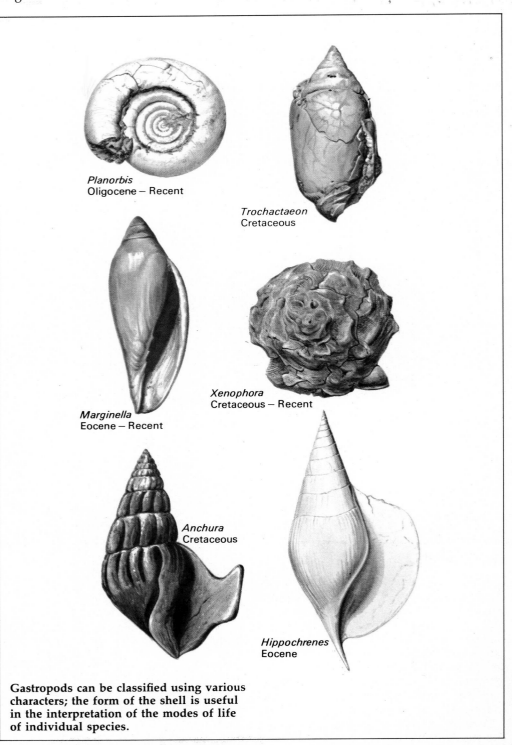

Planorbis
Oligocene – Recent

Trochactaeon
Cretaceous

Marginella
Eocene – Recent

Xenophora
Cretaceous – Recent

Anchura
Cretaceous

Hippochrenes
Eocene

Gastropods can be classified using various characters; the form of the shell is useful in the interpretation of the modes of life of individual species.

Capulus, as its name suggests, is cap-shaped with a large rounded to irregular aperture. This gastropod is relatively abundant in Palaeozoic rocks and was a bottom-dwelling genus feeding on detritus.

Above right: **Fossil ammonites from the Solnhofen Limestone of the Upper Jurassic of Southern Germany.**

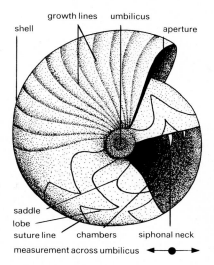

shell | growth lines | umbilicus | aperture
saddle
lobe
suture line | chambers | siphonal neck
measurement across umbilicus

Above: **The structure of a typical cephalopod.**

Right: **Ammonites are important as zone fossils for dating Mesozoic rocks as they changed rapidly with time and were widely distributed. All these ammonites – except *Phylloceras* and *Lytoceras* – are only to be found in Lower Jurassic rocks.**

the northerly Boreal area the belemnites (Carboniferous – Eocene) were more common. These cephalopods have a bullet-like internal skeleton and are closely related to the cuttlefishes, octopuses and squids. Unlike the nautiloids and ammonoids, with four gills, these groups are characterised by only two.

Of the remaining mollusc classes the tooth-shells or scaphopods (Ordovician – Recent) are poorly known throughout the stratigraphic record.

Lytoceras

Phylloceras

Arnioceras

Promicroceras

Asteroceras

Amaltheus

Dactylioceras

5 cm

Invertebrates

Arthropoda

Jointed limbs and a tough outer skeleton are the two major characteristics of the phylum Arthropoda. Variety is also a feature with spiders, insects, centipedes, crabs, lobsters, barnacles and ostracods all included within the phylum, and the success of groups such as the insects is quite spectacular with almost a million species recorded since the early Devonian.

The arthropods first appear in the Cambrian and probably share a common ancestor with the annelid worms. During the Cambrian the story of the arthropods belongs with the trilobites and related sister groups. The trilobites, which are now extinct, were segmented animals whose skeletons were subdivided into three distinct lobes. Certain trilobites such as *Agnostus* and *Trinucleus* were blind mud ingestors or filter feeders; *Dudleyaspis* was an active 'browser', whilst *Deiphon*, a spiny form, was adapted to a planktonic mode of life. The trilobites are used as stratigraphic indicators for the Cambrian. Palaeontologists have also established that trilobites lived in distinct geographic associations known as faunal provinces.

Of the groups directly related to the trilobites, the trilobitoids of the Middle Cambrian – Devonian are of particular interest. Best known from the Middle Cambrian Burgess Shale of Canada, these animals have rather bizarre shapes. *Burgessia*, for example, has a large convex carapace and a long tail spine. It resembles a horseshoe crab whereas *Marrella*

splendens, with four backwardly directed spines and a segmented body, has no modern equivalent. Other arthropods, including the horseshoe crabs and ostracods, can be traced back to Cambrian ancestors. The water scorpions, which include some of the largest known jointed-limbed animals, and the barnacles first appear in the Ordovician. Insects, centipedes and spiders had become common representatives of terrestrial faunas by the Upper Carboniferous and Permian.

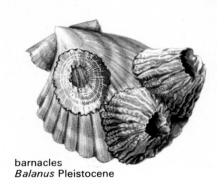

barnacles
Balanus Pleistocene

Cypridea Jurassic –
Cretaceous
freshwater

Cythereis
Jurassic –
Cretaceous
marine

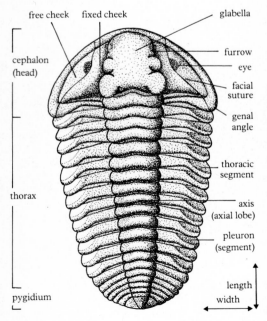

insect in amber

Barnacles *(top)*, **insects** *(left)*, **ostracods,** *(above)* **and trilobites are all representatives of the jointed-limbed arthropods. Only the trilobites have become extinct.**

Trilobite dorsal view

free cheek   fixed cheek   glabella

cephalon (head)

furrow
eye
facial suture
genal angle

thoracic segment

thorax

axis (axial lobe)

pleuron (segment)

length
width

pygidium

Above: **Dorsal view of a typical trilobite.**

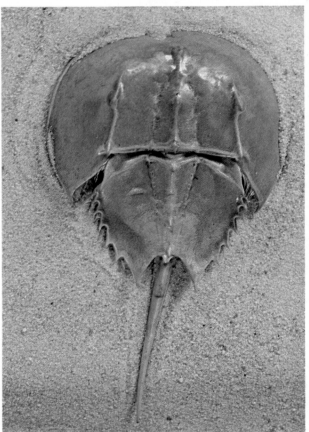

Paedeumias Cambrian
protoparian trilobite

Trilobites were especially abundant during the Cambrian. Various genera and species are used as index fossils during this period.

Left: **A living king crab, Limulus. This ancient group of arthropods, resembling the trilobites, can be traced back to the Cambrian.**

Insects first appeared over 350 million years ago. The earliest species were wingless, but by the Carboniferous huge winged forms such as *Meganeura* had appeared. This panorama illustrates the variety of insects that evolved during the Upper Palaeozoic.
1 Blattodea – cockroach nymph;
2 Palaeodictyoptera – *Lithomantis*

carbonaria; 3 Protodonata – *Meganeura monyi*; 4 Megasecoptera – *Corydaloides seudderi*; 5 Palaeodictyoptera – *Homaloneura ornata*; 6 Blattodea – *Phylloblatta carbonaria*; 7 *Dictyomylaeris poipaulti*; 8 Protorthoptera – *Gerarus danielsi*; 9 Plecoptera – stonefly nymph under water; 10 Protoelytroptera – *Protodytron permianum*; 11 Plecoptera –

Lemmatrophora typica; 12 *Eryops* – one of the first amphibians; 13 Ephemeroptera (mayfly) – *Protereisma permianum*; 14 Orthoptera (grasshopper) – *Metoedischia* spp; 15 Plectopera (stonefly) – *Permocapnia brevipes*; 16 Protohemiptera (plant-sucking bugs) – *Eugereon böckingi*.

Invertebrates

Echinodermata

Unlike the arthropods, the echinoderms or 'spiny-skinned' animals are found only in marine environments. Living echinoderms include the starfish, brittle stars, sea-urchins, sea-lilies and sea-cucumbers. All possess evidence of an internal skeleton, the calcareous plates or ossicles of which are deposited in the middle of mesodermal layer of tissue. Echinoderms can be divided for descriptive purposes into two groups related to their preferred modes of life.

The first group, the so-called 'fixed' echinoderms, include the sea-lilies (crinoids) and extinct stemmed forms such as the cystoids, blastoids and eocrinoids. The crinoids are the most important of the 'fixed' stocks and during the Palaeozoic their plates and ossicles contribute to the formation of various limestones. Most crinoids were and are either current-seeking or current-avoiding. The former live in shallow, high energy waters, whilst the latter rest in quieter niches with their arms spread to gather falling particles of food.

Of the 'free-living' echinoderms the sea urchins (echinoids) are sea-floor dwellers which filter the sediment for food. The earliest echinoids from the Ordovician had flexible tests with overlapping skeletal plates and from these, forms with rigid tests and a regular arrangement of plates arose. Regular echinoids related to the living *Cidaris* were abundant during the Palaeozoic.

The cidaroids thrived during the Mesozoic but the dominant echinoids of this and the Cainozoic Era are irregular genera such as *Pygaster*, *Micraster* and *Mellita*.

Starfish and brittle stars first appeared in the Palaeozoic. They probably arose from a crinoid-type ancestor and evolved to fill the roles of mollusc-eating predators and bottom scavengers. Starfish beds within the geological column reflect the gregarious nature of these animals in specific food-rich environments.

Top: **Sea-lilies or crinoids are fixed-stemmed echinoderms that lived on the sea floor.**

Right: **Starfish and brittle stars are free-living echinoderms that are still a successful part of the marine community today.**

Left: **Hemicideris is an example of an echinoid – these were gregarious marine animals that reached a peak of diversity during the Palaeozoic era.**

Periechocrinites
Ordovician
Carboniferous

Marsupites
Cretaceous

Pentacrinites
Triassic   Pliocene

Sagenocrinites Silurian

Pentasteria
Jurassic
Eocene

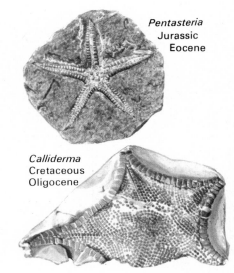

Calliderma
Cretaceous
Oligocene

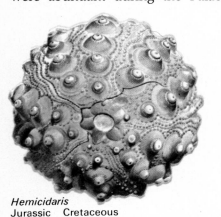

Hemicidaris
Jurassic   Cretaceous

Palaeocoma
Jurassic

Orophocrinus
Carboniferous

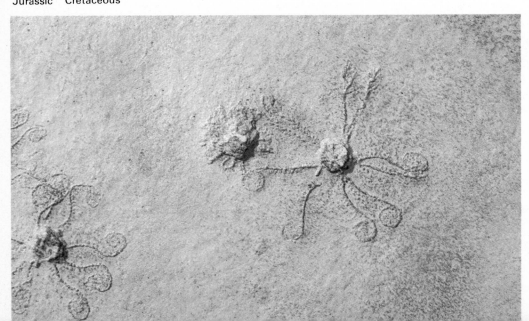

Crinoids preserved in the Upper Jurassic Solnhofen Limestone. The fossils are extremely well preserved as the rapid burial in the soft muds retained even the most intricate details.

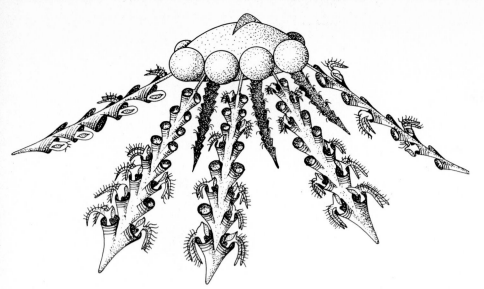

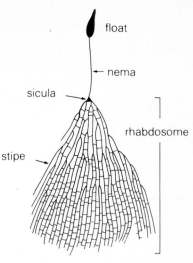

Graptolites

Graptolite fossils can appear very unimpressive when found as white carbonaceous films on the surfaces of shales or slates. However, the complex organic materials that comprise the graptolite skeleton (periderm) may be well enough preserved in fine-grained mudstones to show that it consists of two layers of tissue. Of these, the fusellar tissue is deposited as thin half-rings one on top of the other. The rings are fused along a zig-zag line and form the inner wall of the tubes that make up the colony. External to the fusellar tissue is the fibrous cortical tissue. The half-ring structure of the inner layer is similar to that of the basal tube of the living hemichordate *Rhabdopleura* which suggests close biological affinities with the hemichordates and a distinct link with the vertebrates.

The graptolites were colonial animals that first appeared in the Late Cambrian and evolved rapidly during the Ordovician and Silurian. Palaeontologists recognise two main orders of graptolites: one has many branches and two types of external cup (thecae), whilst the other exhibits a reduction in branches from eight to one and has only one type of thecal unit. The first group are called dendroids, the second graptoloids. *Dendrogaptus* is a dendroid, as is *Dictyonema flabelliforme* which is one of the best known. It has a bell shape with the numerous branches connected by slender crossing bars. It is possible that the organisms inside the thecal cups performed different functions, but combined to help the colony stabilise its position and work with efficiency. Of the graptoloids, many four, two and one-branched species can be found in rocks of the Lower Palaeozoic. Four-branched genera include *Tetragraptus*. *Dicellograptus* is an example of a two-branched graptoloid, whilst *Diplograptus* and *Monograptus* are both single in structure. In *Diplograptus* the thecal cups occur on both sides of the branch or stripe, but in *Monograptus* the cups are on one side only. This condition represents the final stage in a long process of branch reduction coupled with an increase in the side of the individual cups and other functional modifications.

Above: **The colonies of numerous diplograptids have been found attached to a large float structure. This 'multiple' colony is thought to have floated in the surface waters of Lower Palaeozoic seas.**

Above: **The dendroid graptolite, *Dictyonema*. *Below:* A selection of graptolites showing their different growth forms. They are very useful for dating Palaeozoic rocks as they changed rapidly with time and had a world-wide distribution.**

5 cm

Dendrograptus

Diplograptus

Monograptus

Tetragraptus

Dicellograptus

Vertebrates

Evolution of the earliest vertebrates

A vertebrate is any animal that has a hard, narrow supporting structure extending along its back; in most cases it consists of true bone and is segmented. The first animals referred to as vertebrates are recorded from the early Ordovician. Known only from fragments of bone, scales, and plates they are regarded as the earliest representatives of the jawless fishes. Their remains provide evidence of an early origin of vertebrate stocks but are of limited value in our quest for information on their likely ancestors.

The lower chordates are the most likely ancestors to the vertebrates. Unfortunately, they are poorly known in the fossil record except for the graptolites, and their roles in the evolution of the vertebrates are interpreted essentially on zoological evidence. Chordates are recognised by the presence of a stiff rod of tissue running along the length of the body beneath the nerve cord. This is the notochord and it is clearly seen in the living *Amphioxus*. Graptolites, *Rhabdopleura* and the acorn worms have only a small notochord at the front of the body and are thus termed hemichordates. It is possible that the true chordates arose from a hemichordate ancestor such as an acorn worm, which in turn could be derived from an echinoderm.

Larval stages are important in the understanding of evolutionary successions and it is remarkable how close the larvae of an echinoderm and an acorn worm, such as *Balanoglossus*, are in terms of their anatomy. A free-swimming ancestor for the first jawless fishes could seem essential and either *Amphioxus* or the larval stage of a sea squirt would perhaps suffice.

The potential of an echinoderm ancestry for the vertebrates has been considered in detail, and attention has focussed on the calcichordates, a bizarre stock from the Ordovician. They are calcite-plated with a flattened body (theca), a distinct 'tail', structures similar to the gill slits of the vertebrates and in addition a well-developed brain. A succession of calcichordates progressively exhibit characteristics of a more advanced nature and it is thought that this lineage could provide a number of points from which all chordates could have arisen.

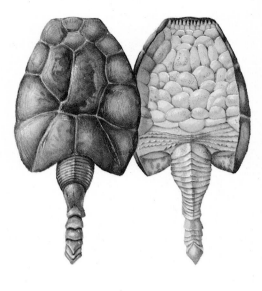

The calcichordate *Mitrocystella* was a flattened, assymetrical animal with a short tail and plates on one side of its body. The calcichordates may have given rise to the chordates.

A living acorn worm. These primitive chordates provide an insight into the possible evolution of the chordates from an echinoderm ancestor.

Fishes

The primitive jawless fishes evolved rapidly during the Silurian and Devonian and numerous representatives of the 'shell-skinned' ostracoderms are recorded from the latter period, of which *Anglaspis* is one example. A small sucker-like mouth on the undersurface of the head indicates that these creatures fed on organic debris scattered over the sediment surface. It is likely that the first ostracoderms lived in the seas, but during the Devonian various species invaded the mouths of rivers and streams. The modern lampreys and hagfishes are relatives of the Palaeozoic ostracoderms. Unlike their relatives they have lost the armour plating and have adapted to a semi-parasitic life on other fishes.

Modifications of the gill arches and the forward skull region resulted in the appearance of the first jawed fishes in the Silurian. The jaw also possessed teeth and this association resulted in the development of meat-eating habits and a host of predator species. Heavily armoured fishes, the placoderms, flourished during the Devonian period with

the 'jointed-necked' arthrodires attaining lengths of 7–8m (26ft). These huge creatures ruled the Devonian seas, whilst the related but smaller antiarchs, such as *Bothriolepsis* and *Coccosteus*, adapted to an exclusively freshwater mode of life.

It is thought that the placoderms are related to the cartilaginous fishes such as the sharks and rays. These, too, are predators and their earliest representatives appear in the Middle Devonian. By the Upper Devonian the early shark, *Clado-selache*, had appeared and its similarities to modern sharks suggest that the group was and still is ideally suited to its mode of life.

Bony fishes are recorded from the Upper Silurian and by the Middle Devonian had diversified considerably. Two groups, the ray-finned (actinopterygians) and lobe-finned (crossopterygians) fishes can be differentiated by the Middle Devonian, with the latter containing representative of the lungfishes, coelocanths and extinct rhipidistians. Of these, the rhipidistians, including the *Eustheno-teron*, were comparatively short-lived but

their anatomy suggests that they were closely linked with the evolution of the Amphibia.

The ray-finned, bony fishes are the most diversified of all fish groups. At first they were streamlined hunter-killers but as time progressed various species adapted to different modes of life and occupied a host of new niches. Trends included the shortening of the jaw, the development of a swim-bladder, thinner scales and an enhanced symmetry of the tail. By the Cretaceous tarpon and herring-like fishes were common along with relatives of the salmon, trout, perch, plaice and mackerel. During the Cainozoic, bony fishes such as the carp, minnow and catfish had evolved in freshwater environments.

The evolution of the fishes from their beginnings in the Silurian and Devonian periods to the present day.

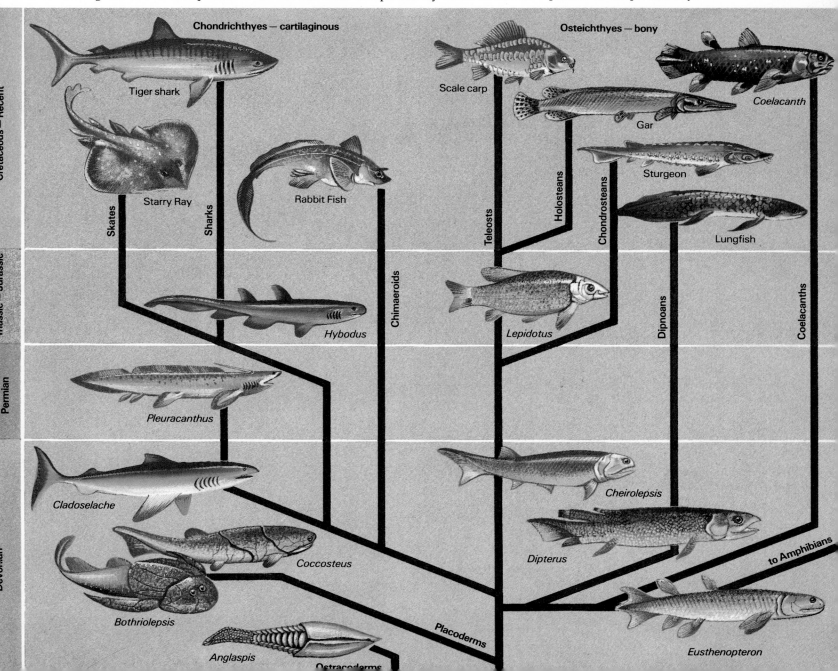

Amphibians

The origin of the amphibians is closely linked with the rhipidistian fishes. These lobe-finned forms had a reduced number of plates in the central or crown region of the skull and possessed teeth with a complexly folded or labyrinthine structure. The reduction in skull bones is an essential prerequisite in an amphibian ancestor and the first amphibians do also possess labyrinthodont teeth. Another feature of the rhipidistians, particularly

Amphibians without labyrinthine teeth also thrived during the Carboniferous. They belonged to a group called the lepospondyls, small amphibians characterised by vertebrae in which the centrum, or unit below the spinal cord, is a single bone. Of the lepospondyls, *Ophiderpeton* was rather snake-like, whilst *Microbrachis*, with its small limbs, had a newt-like appearance.

The amphibians flourished in the Per-

mian but with the advent of the reptiles they became less important in most vertebrate communities. The archaic amphibians of the Palaeozoic finally disappeared in the Triassic. From the Palaeozoic onwards, however, the modern amphibians which had evolved from the lepospondyls began to diversify. Frogs and toads, newts and salamanders had all appeared by the Upper Cretaceous; the first frog arose in the Triassic.

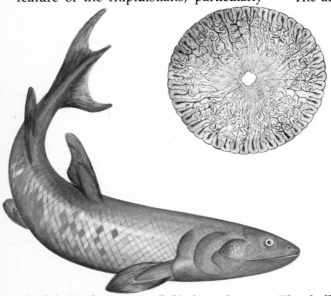

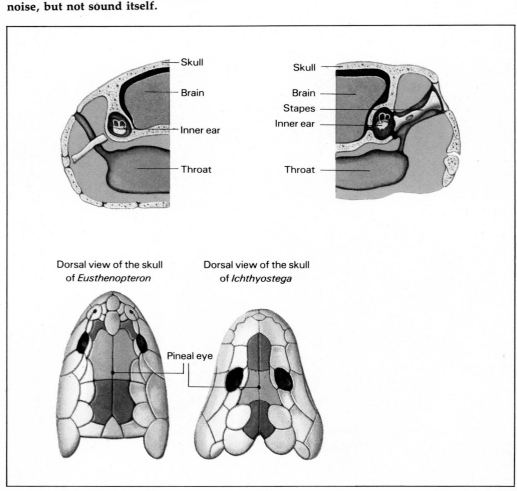

The fish *Eusthenopteron* (left) showed some important developments which heralded the amphibians. The infolding of its teeth's outer enamel is identical to that found in the teeth of *Ichthyostega* (right), the first amphibian.

The skulls of *Eusthenopteron* and *Ichthyostega* show strong similarities. One of the major differences concerns the structure of the ear. The fish ear is much more basic and can detect vibrations from noise, but not sound itself.

Eusthenopteron and *Sauripterus*, is the reduction of bones within the fins which is an important stage in the development of limbs.

The first amphibian, *Ichthyostega*, is recorded from the Upper Devonian. It retains some of the primitive characters of its fish ancestors but has developed four stout limbs. The skull of *Ichthyostega* is broad and flat and the jaws are lined by strong, sharp teeth. The first amphibians lived along the shorelines, swamps and lakes. They were carnivores with fish and possibly insects and other arthropods as part of their diet.

Throughout the Upper Devonian and Lower Carboniferous the amphibians showed considerable potential and diversified to fill many niches. By the Upper Carboniferous the amphibians were abundant, with the swamps and coal-forming forests providing ideal wet-humid conditions. Even the largest amphibians cannot stray far from water: they live a double life and water is the essential medium in which their eggs are laid and the larval stage develops. The amphibians of the Carboniferous include the long-bodied *Eogyrinus*, *Loxomma* and *Megalocephalus*. All three animals possessed the labyrinthodont type of tooth and were probably direct descendants of *Ichthyostega*.

Skull
Brain
Inner ear
Throat

Skull
Brain
Stapes
Inner ear
Throat

Dorsal view of the skull of *Eusthenopteron*

Dorsal view of the skull of *Ichthyostega*

Pineal eye

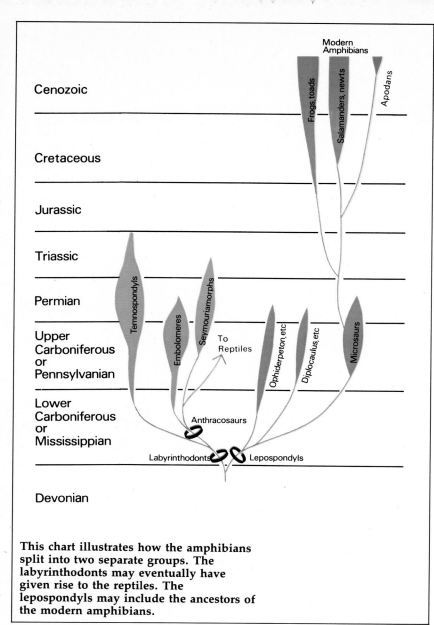

Cenozoic	Modern Amphibians
Cretaceous	Frogs, toads / Salamanders, newts / Apodans
Jurassic	
Triassic	
Permian	Temnospondyls / Seymouriamorphs
Upper Carboniferous or Pennsylvanian	Embolomeres / To Reptiles / Ophiderpeton, etc / Diplocaulus, etc / Microsaurs
Lower Carboniferous or Mississippian	Anthracosaurs / Labyrinthodonts / Lepospondyls
Devonian	

This chart illustrates how the amphibians split into two separate groups. The labyrinthodonts may eventually have given rise to the reptiles. The lepospondyls may include the ancestors of the modern amphibians.

A group of early amphibians: *Seymouria* (Permian North America), *Cyclotosaurus* (Triassic), *Peltobrachis* (Permian East Africa), *Cardiocephalus* and *Diplocaulus* (Permian North America) and the carnivorous South American toad (still in existence).

Seymouria

Salamander-like fossil larvae branchiosaurs.

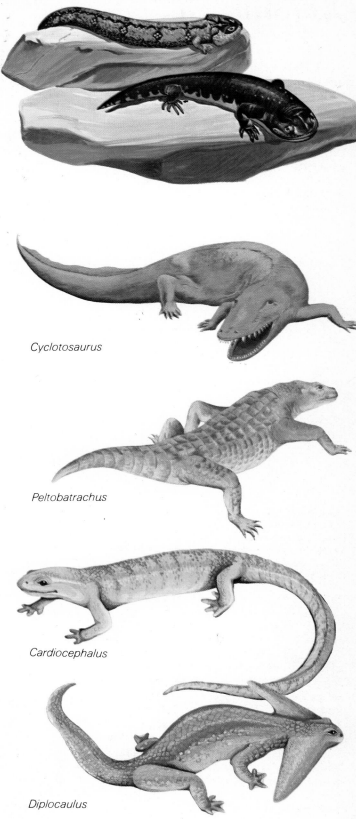

Cyclotosaurus

Peltobatrachus

Cardiocephalus

Diplocaulus

carnivorous South American toad

Reptiles

Unlike the amphibians, reptiles have a scaly skin and lay eggs with a tough leathery or mineralised shell. These two characteristics free the reptiles from the need to return to water or live in a humid environment.

The reptilian egg is one of the major advances in the evolution of the vertebrates. Its structure provides a protective environment for the developing embryo. The outer shell prevents desiccation and yet allows the embryo to breathe air and get rid of carbon dioxide. The embryo is surrounded within the shell by several membranes. Of these the amnion encloses the embryo in its own watery environment whilst the allantois acts as a lung for breathing and the chorion is a protective membrane. Food for the developing embryo is stored in the yolk sac.

The first reptile, *Hylonomus*, evolved in the Upper Carboniferous. Its development was probably linked with the pressures that existed within the amphibian-dominated communities of that time. To protect itself, *Hylonomus* lived in the tree stumps around the swamp edges, where it also laid its eggs. By the Permian several major groups of reptiles had evolved. These included the direct descendants of *Hylonomus*, reptiles with a complete or solid skull roof in which the only openings are for the eyes and nostrils. Such reptiles are called *anapsids*. *Synapsids*, or reptiles with a single opening behind the eye (see below) and *diapsids*, with two openings, also appear in the Permian. The last group of reptiles, characterised by a skull with a small single opening, appear in the early Triassic. These are termed *euryapsids*, and they include sea-going reptiles such as pla-codonts, ichthyosaurs and pleisiosaurs.

The anapsid reptiles, or cotylosaurs are of limited importance in post-Permian communities, but in the Triassic they gave rise to the successful turtles and tortoises. These first appear in the swampland environments of southern Germany, with the distinctively shelled *Proganochelys* living along the water edge. Riverine and marine turtles appeared in the Upper Jurassic – Lower Cretaceous: *Archelon*, from the Upper Cretaceous, was the largest turtle known to man. It grew to 5m in length and was adapted to an open marine life. During the Cainozoic, sea turtles flourish whilst both marsh and land-dwelling forms underwent a considerable diversification.

Of the diapsids, the Permian representative are poorly known but during the Triassic various stocks of archosaurs or

Below: **Hylonomus, one of the earliest reptiles, from the Carboniferous of Canada.**

Bottom: **Hypsognathus was an insectivorous anapsid.**

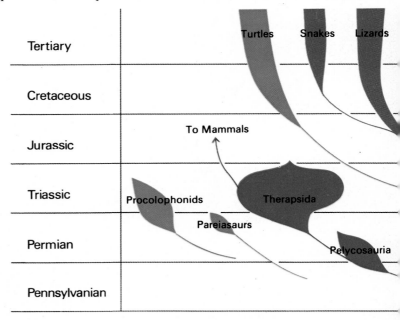

The main lines of reptilian evolution can be traced by the differing skull types.

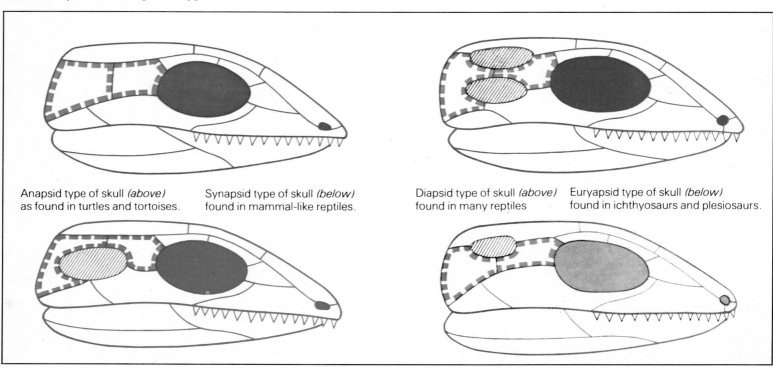

Anapsid type of skull *(above)* as found in turtles and tortoises.

Synapsid type of skull *(below)* found in mammal-like reptiles.

Diapsid type of skull *(above)* found in many reptiles

Euryapsid type of skull *(below)* found in ichthyosaurs and plesiosaurs.

wn-reptiles' appeared throughout the orld. Early genera included the small nsect-eating *Millerosaurus* and the larger (1.5m) fish-eating *Proterosuchus*. Gradually, through minor modifications and adaptations, the diapsids began to challenge the mammal-like reptiles. Changes in position of the limbs resulted in a longer stride and the loss of the primitive, restrictive sprawling gait of earlier forms. In time the thecodontians or 'teeth-in-socket' archosaurs, of which *Proterosuchus* is a representative, began to dominate vertebrate communities and from them the dinosaurs, the most advanced of all reptiles, evolved. The thecodontians were also ancestral to the crocodiles and pterosaurs. The pterosaurs are now extinct but during the Mesozoic they were the rulers of the air. Some pterosaurs were no larger than a sparrow (*Pterodactylus*) whilst others including *Pteranodon* and *Quetzalcoatlus* had wingspans of 7 and 15 metres respectively.

The real key to success on land was the development of the reptilian egg which meant that there was no need to return to water in order to breed. The egg shown here is a developing turtle egg and shows the embryonic membranes.

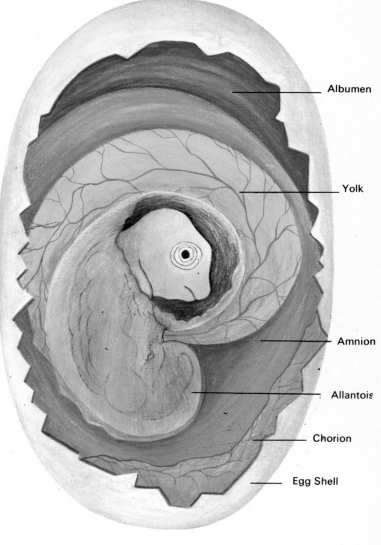

Albumen

Yolk

Amnion

Allantois

Chorion

Egg Shell

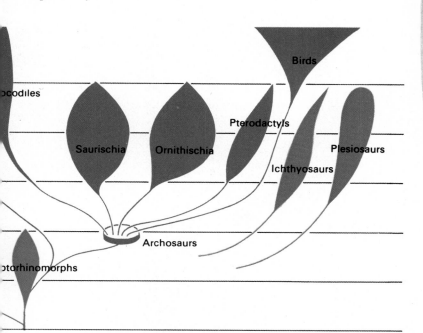

Above: **The chart indicates the range and relative importance of various reptile groups since the Upper Carboniferous.**

The turtles and tortoises first appeared in the Triassic and have undergone comparitively few modifications since that time. **Archelon** was a huge turtle that measured 4 metres in length. **Proganochelys**, an early turtle, lived along the water edge and was approximately 60 centimetres long.

Sea-turtle

Land-tortoise

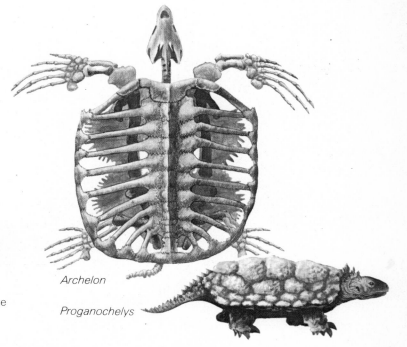

Archelon

Proganochelys

Sea-going reptiles

Many of the reptiles that returned to an aquatic mode of life during the Mesozoic were euryapsids, including the ichthyosaurs, placodonts and plesiosaurs. Prior to this the earliest aquatic reptiles were the slimly built mesosaurs of the late Carboniferous – early Permian. *Mesosaurus* and its relatives lived in fresh water lakes and swam with the air of a long, laterally flattened tail. Its long jaws were lined by sharp teeth whilst the limbs were slightly paddle-like in form. The mesosaurs fed on fish and small crustaceans.

In contrast to the mesosaurs, the dolphin-like ichthyosaurs and their mixosaurian ancestors were fishlike and ideally adapted to a sea dwelling mode of life. A typical ichthyosaur had a short body, a long beak, a large symmetrical caudal fin and paddle-like limbs. Ichthyosaurs were powerful swimmers and the major marine predators of the Jurassic period.

Placodonts were confined to the Triassic and were adapted to a life in shallow coastal waters where they fed on bivalve molluscs. *Placodus* had a rather elongate body and normal, but webbed limbs. Its head, however, was quite remarkable as it bore heavy peg-like teeth on the muzzle and large crushing teeth over both the upper palate and lower jaw. It was with these that it loosened, freed and crushed its food.

The webbed feet and long tails of certain placodonts suggest an aquatic mode of life. The strong, flat palate teeth (seen in the skull below) were used to crush seashells.

The huge jaws of the mosasaurs were highly effective in capturing their prey, such as marine turtles.

The first discovery of a mosasaur was made in 1770, when the huge jaws of a 'Meuse Lizard' were extracted from the Upper Cretaceous rocks of St Peter's Mountain, Maastricht in the Netherlands.

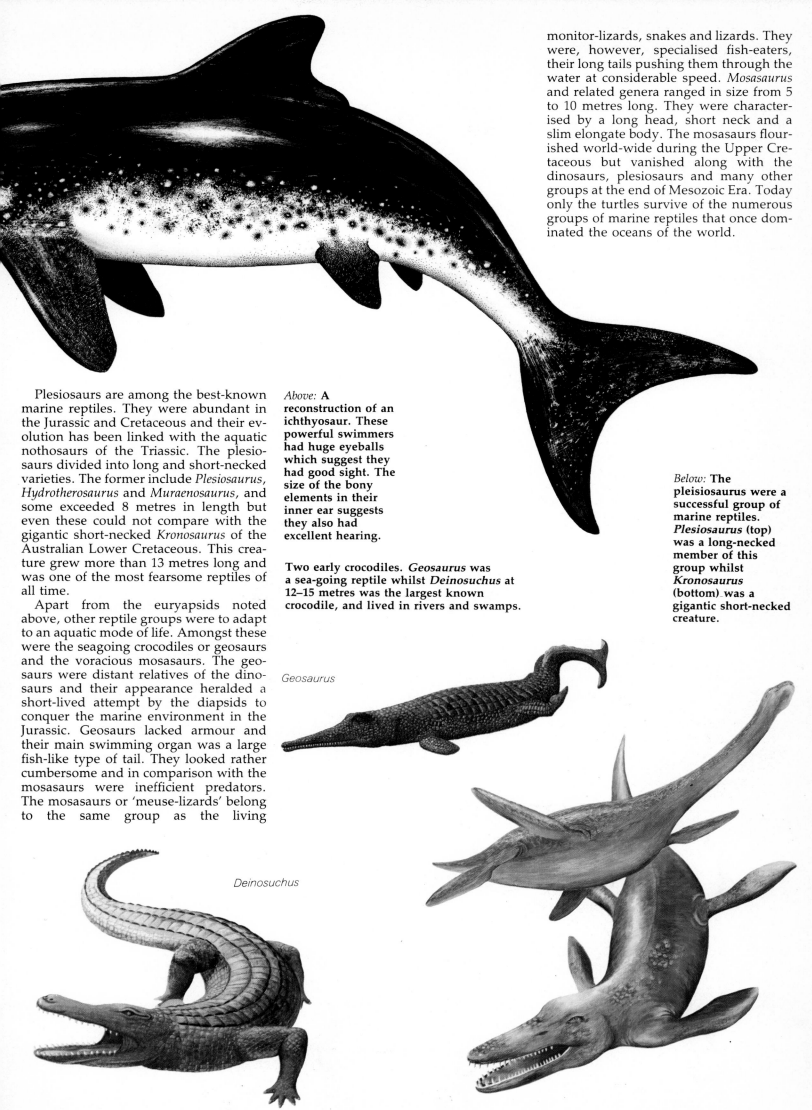

monitor-lizards, snakes and lizards. They were, however, specialised fish-eaters, their long tails pushing them through the water at considerable speed. *Mosasaurus* and related genera ranged in size from 5 to 10 metres long. They were characterised by a long head, short neck and a slim elongate body. The mosasaurs flourished world-wide during the Upper Cretaceous but vanished along with the dinosaurs, plesiosaurs and many other groups at the end of Mesozoic Era. Today only the turtles survive of the numerous groups of marine reptiles that once dominated the oceans of the world.

Plesiosaurs are among the best-known marine reptiles. They were abundant in the Jurassic and Cretaceous and their evolution has been linked with the aquatic nothosaurs of the Triassic. The plesiosaurs divided into long and short-necked varieties. The former include *Plesiosaurus*, *Hydrotherosaurus* and *Muraenosaurus*, and some exceeded 8 metres in length but even these could not compare with the gigantic short-necked *Kronosaurus* of the Australian Lower Cretaceous. This creature grew more than 13 metres long and was one of the most fearsome reptiles of all time.

Apart from the euryapsids noted above, other reptile groups were to adapt to an aquatic mode of life. Amongst these were the seagoing crocodiles or geosaurs and the voracious mosasaurs. The geosaurs were distant relatives of the dinosaurs and their appearance heralded a short-lived attempt by the diapsids to conquer the marine environment in the Jurassic. Geosaurs lacked armour and their main swimming organ was a large fish-like type of tail. They looked rather cumbersome and in comparison with the mosasaurs were inefficient predators. The mosasaurs or 'meuse-lizards' belong to the same group as the living

Above: **A reconstruction of an ichthyosaur. These powerful swimmers had huge eyeballs which suggest they had good sight. The size of the bony elements in their inner ear suggests they also had excellent hearing.**

Two early crocodiles. *Geosaurus* was a sea-going reptile whilst *Deinosuchus* at 12–15 metres was the largest known crocodile, and lived in rivers and swamps.

Below: **The pleisiosaurus were a successful group of marine reptiles. *Plesiosaurus* (top) was a long-necked member of this group whilst *Kronosaurus* (bottom) was a gigantic short-necked creature.**

Geosaurus

Deinosuchus

Dinosaurs

Although it is generally accepted that the dinosaurs evolved from thecodontian stock there is some doubt as to the relationship of the two major groups of dinosaurs. The question is whether or not the two evolved separately from a thecodontian or from a common, intermediate dinosaurian ancestor. The groups are defined on the structure of the pelvis with that of the 'lizard-hipped' saurischians having a rather more primitive form than that of the 'bird-hipped' ornithischians. In the saurischians the pelvis is essentially three-pronged with the pubis directed forwards and downwards. Ornithischian pelves have a four-pronged appearance with the main component of the pubis directed backwards beneath the ischium. Strangely, both types allow for the development of four and two-legged species and all dinosaurs were much more mobile than the thecodonts with their limbs drawn beneath the body so that a more efficient and larger stride was possible.

The dinosaurs asssumed the role of dominant reptiles in the Middle and Upper Triassic. Saurischians and ornithischians appear simultaneously in South African and South American communities and soon spread northwards into Europe and North America. The saurischians of the Triassic include both carnivorous and herbivorous animals. The meat-eaters were representatives of the carnosaurs and coelurosaurs, the herbivores were prosauropods. All ornithischians were plant eaters.

Until quite recently it was thought that the ornithischians evolved later than their saurischians cousins. The discoveries of *Fabrosaurus* and *Heterodontosaurus* have revised that belief and the idea that the first bird-hipped species were four-legged. Both animals are recorded from the Triassic of southern Africa. Amongst their descendants were *Camptosaurus, Iguanodon, Hypsilophodon,* the duck-billed and bone-headed dinosaurs. All of them were bipedal creatures.

The major diversification of the ornithopods took place in the Upper Cretaceous when numerous duck-billed species evolved from the 'normal' iguanodont line. Their bodies were similar to that of their ancestors although they had webbed fingers and hoof-like feet. Unlike *Iguanodon*, the skulls of the duck-billed dinosaurs were rather bizarre with broad flattened snouts and distinctive crests. The duck-billed dinosaurs were herd animals and it is possible that their facial features helped recognition.

Amongst the bone-headed or pachycephalosaur dinosaurs, territorial battles were probably quite frequent. The presence of a bony helmet was the diagnostic feature of these animals and it is assumed that its purpose was the same as that of the thickened skulls in mountain sheep or goats. Amongst these animals, the

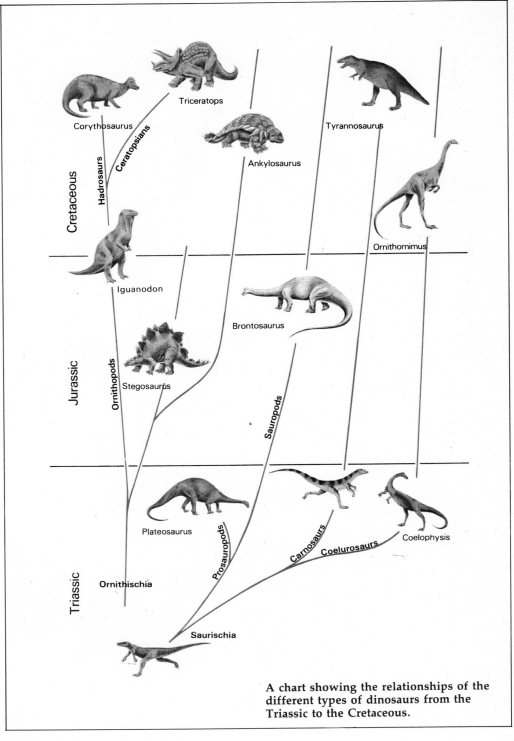

A chart showing the relationships of the different types of dinosaurs from the Triassic to the Cretaceous.

The two major groups of dinosaurs are defined by the structure of their pelvis. The 'lizard-hipped' saurischians have a more primitive structure than the 'bird-hipped' ornithischians.

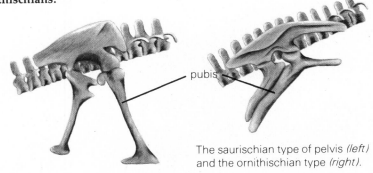

The saurischian type of pelvis *(left)* and the ornithischian type *(right)*.

dominant males clashed in mighty battles during the mating season.

Four-legged ornithischians first appeared during the early Jurassic. The earliest genus was *Scelidosaurus*, the 'limb-lizard', which some workers believe is ancestral to both the plated stegosaurs and armoured ankylosaurs. It had a small head, long neck and numerous bony plates embedded in the skin. At 4 metres long it was approximately two-thirds the size of the *Stegosaurus*, which is the best known of the plated lizards and was well represented during the Upper Jurassic. It is possible that the hollow plates arranged along the back of the 'roof-lizard' functioned as heat regulators by absorbing the rays of the sun in the morning and losing heat through radiation when the animal was too warm. The stegosaurs were relatively shortlived and during the Cretaceous the ceratopsians and ankylosaurs were the dominant four-legged ornithischians. The ankylosaurs were squat, heavy creatures with *Ankylosaurus*, the 'reptilian tank', weighing 3 tonnes. During an attack the ankylosaurs would lie down and present an impregnable target to a would-be predator. In contrast, the horned cera- topsians would have charged at their antagonist. Speed, herding and the possession of a large bony frill were all important features in the success of the horned dinosaurs against predation. The first ceratopsian was *Protoceratops* from the Lower Cretaceous; it was 2 metres long and weighed approximately 1·5 tonnes. During the Upper Cretaceous, the ceratopsians were extremely successful and numerous species evolved over a short period of time. *Triceratops* and *Styracosaurus* were amongst the largest of these dinosaurs. The former grew to 11 metres long and weighed 8·5 tonnes.

The dinosaurs were a highly successful group of reptiles. This page illustrates some members of the various groups. *Plateosaurus* **and** *Brachiosaurus* **were huge swamp-dwelling saurischians;** *Iguanodon* **and the hadrosaurs represent two branches of the ornithischians. The bone-headed pachycephalosaurs were a later group of dinosaurs that are mainly recorded from the Upper Cretaceous.** *Stegosaurus* **was an ornithischian of the Jurassic period, the ankylosaurs were an armour-plated group that are found in the Cretaceous.** *Tricerotops***, was a member of the ceratopsians which were effectively the last successful group of ornithischians.**

Brachiosaurus

Plateosaurus

Iguanodon

Hadrosaur

Head of *Pachycephalosaurus*

Stegosaurus (left)
Ankylosaurus (below)

Triceratops

Dinosaurs

The importance of the ornithischians during the Cretaceous was matched by the saurischians during the Jurassic. From Triassic ancestors, various two and four-legged carnivores and herbivores evolved. The carnivores belonged to the carnosaur and coelurosaurian lineages, both of which are included in the suborder Theropoda. *Megalosaurus* and *Dilophosaurus* from the Lower Jurassic are amongst the earliest of the giant meateaters. Their line of evolution ends in *Tyrannosaurus*, the greatest predator of all time. Amongst the coelurosaurs, the variety of small bipedal animals was greater with different genera adapted to scavenging, nest robbing and killing. *Coelophysis* from the Upper Triassic of Mexico was an active predator, whilst *Ornithomimus*, an ostrich-like dinosaur, fed on eggs, small dinosaurs, fruit and insects. Large brained coelurosaurs with stereoscopic vision are recorded from the Cretaceous, and include *Deinonychus*, the 'terrible-claw', and *Saurornithoides*. It is thought that the birds arose from a small coelurosaurian ancestor.

Apart from *Tyrannosaurus*, the best known dinosaurs include *Brachiosaurus*, a huge four-legged saurischian that thrived in lowland and swampland areas in the Upper Jurassic. It was 12 metres tall and 23 metres long. It weighed 81 tonnes and was one of the largest animals ever to have lived on earth.

The sauropods were most common during the Jurassic but various species persisted throughout the Cretaceous Period. They were mostly adapted to a life in water, with the tremendous weight of the body supported by the enclosing medium. Their long necks allowed them to browse from overhanging trees or scoop soft weed from the lake surface. Like all other dinosaurs, the sauropods vanished in the Late Cretaceous approximately 140 million years after the appearance of the first dinosaur species.

Tyrannosaurus rex, 'the largest flesh-eating animal that ever walked the Earth'.

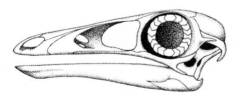

The head of *Ornithomimus* was similar to that of the ostrich. The animal had no teeth and the jaws were beak-like.

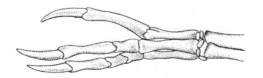

The three-fingered hand of *Ornithomimus* was similar to that of several other coelurosaurs and was used for grasping and lifting food materials.

Ornithomimus, the 'bird imitator', was an 'ostrich-like dinosaur' which lived approximately 100–70 million years ago.

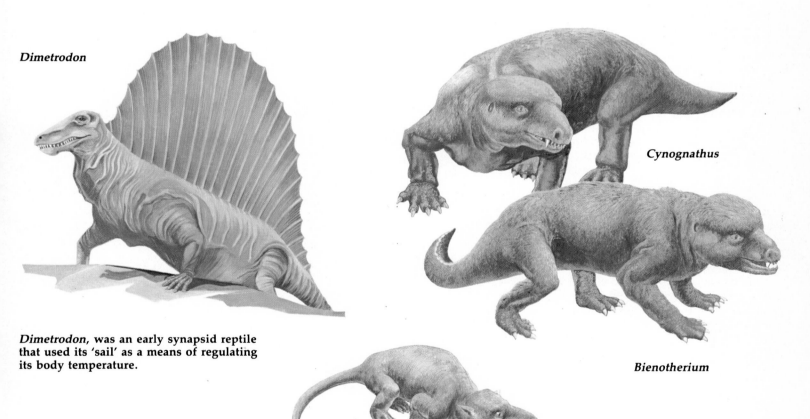

Dimetrodon

Dimetrodon, was an early synapsid reptile that used its 'sail' as a means of regulating its body temperature.

Cynognathus

Bienotherium

Oligokyphus

Top: **Some advanced coelurosaurs, including *Saurornithoides*, were adapted to hunt small mammals in the poor light of early evening.**

Above: **The evolution of the mammal-like reptiles is marked by a number of modifications to the skeleton. The general trend was towards slimmer bones and an improved dentition. Attempts to regulate body temperature were successful and it is likely that later species were warm-blooded and covered in hair. *Cynognathus* was about the size of a pig and, like *Bienotherium*, lived in the Triassic: *Oligokyphus* was about 50 cm long and survived into the Jurassic.**

Mammal-like reptiles

Synapsid reptiles (the eventual ancestors of the mammals) rivalled and eventually dominated the anapsids in terrestrial communities. During the Permian, sail-backed genera, such as *Dimetrodon* and *Edaphosaurus*, were prominent. Their sails, supported by long vertebral spines, had a temperature regulating role. Temperature regulation is a feature of synapsid evolution, its gradual refinement enabling a succession of mammal-like reptiles, known as therapsids, to occupy the major roles in Upper Permian and early Triassic communities. Tell-tale 'whisker' pits suggest that some mammal-like reptiles were hair-covered and probably warm-blooded. By the Upper Triassic the first mammals had arisen

from a synapsid ancestor.

Amongst the various evolutionary trends exhibited by the mammal-like reptiles, changes in dentition and limb structure rank alongside the perfection of temperature regulation in terms of importance. The dental changes involve an overall reduction in the number of teeth, as well as their specialization into incisors, canines and molars for the grasping and cutting of food. Modifications of the limbs and girdles relate to a change away from the primitive sprawling stance. The number of bones in the hands and feet is also reduced. It is probable that the more advanced mammal-like reptiles were almost indistinguishable from their mammalian cousins. It is difficult to believe that they still laid eggs.

Evolution of the birds

Three complete fossil specimens of *Archaeopteryx* have been discovered in Upper Jurassic sediments and each provides a detailed insight into the anatomy of the first bird. Feathers are clearly evident and the arms are extended to support a wing. The head is rather chicken-like but had teeth. The bird also had three claw-like fingers, a wishbone and an opposable first toe which may have helped it perch in trees. *Archaeopteryx* exhibits a mosaic of evolutionary characters and whilst some workers believe it is a preflight creature, others state that 'feathers mean flight'. Birds probably evolved from either the crocodiles or the coelurosaurs, and at present a coelurosaur ancestry seems more likely with a small creature such as *Compsognathus* providing an indication of the possible ancestral link. The presence of teeth and the three fingers could be regarded as the retention of primitive characters.

During the Cretaceous, the evidence for the evolution of the birds is limited. Sea-going genera are recorded from the Upper Cretaceous with the flightless diver *Hesperornis* and the toothed *Ichthyornis* as members of the North American Niobrara Chalk community. By the Eocene, 55 million years ago, numerous families had appeared with cuckoos, pigeons, herons, waders and tropical bird-like species being recorded from the London Clay of south-east England. Large flightless birds also evolved at this time with the 'terror-cranes' or Diatrymiformes assuming the roles of their distant dinosaur cousins. Birds of a more modern character appeared during the Oligocene and giant penguins are recorded from Australia and Antarctica. By the Miocene, rails, ibises, owls, hawks and primitive swifts were well represented in various avifaunas. Pliocene birds included a number of species still found today and ostriches, emus, rheas and tinamous are recorded for the first time. The harsh conditions of the Pleistocene had a significant effect on the geographic distribution of many birds. Glacial periods led to the development of migration patterns, whereas natural barriers such as glaciers, sea-level changes or mountains could have induced isolation and the development of new species.

The structure of a modern bird. Note the wing feathers and skeleton, the keeled sternum and the shortened tail.

A fossil of *Archaeopteryx*. Unlike modern birds, it lacked a sternum and had a long tail. Strong teeth also indicate a close link with a coelurosaurian ancestor.

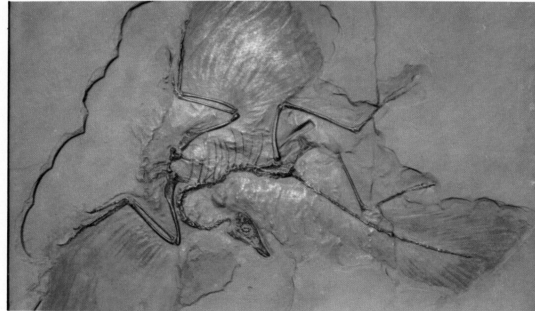

Archaeopteryx **bore a close resemblance to the coelurosaurs, such as *Compsognathus*.**

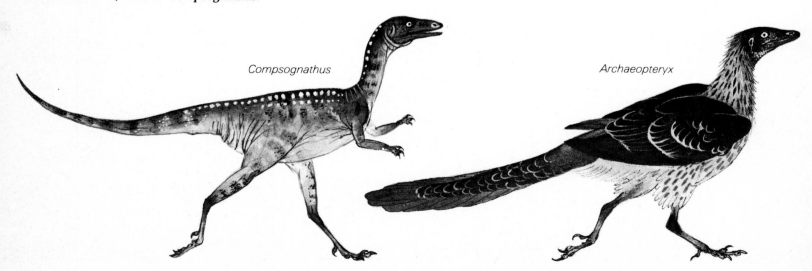

Compsognathus

Archaeopteryx

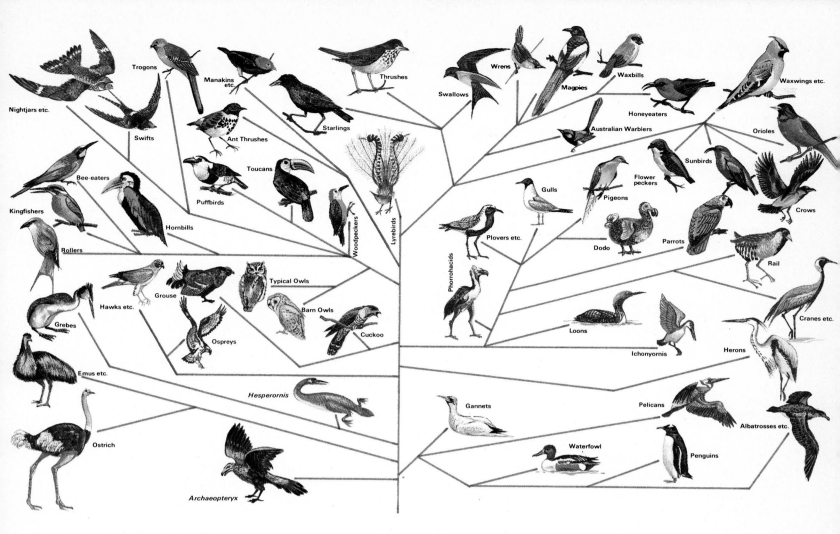

The following labels appear on the family tree illustration:

Nightjars etc.
Trogons
Manakins etc.
Thrushes
Wrens
Waxbills
Magpies
Waxwings etc.
Swallows
Honeyeaters
Swifts
Ant Thrushes
Starlings
Australian Warblers
Orioles
Bee-eaters
Toucans
Sunbirds
Kingfishers
Puffbirds
Flower peckers
Gulls
Pigeons
Rollers
Hornbills
Woodpeckers
Lyrebirds
Plovers etc.
Dodo
Parrots
Crows
Hawks etc.
Grouse
Typical Owls
Phorrohacids
Rail
Grebes
Barn Owls
Ospreys
Cuckoo
Loons
Cranes etc.
Emus etc.
Ichonyornis
Herons
Hesperornis
Gannets
Pelicans
Ostrich
Waterfowl
Penguins
Albatrosses etc.
Archaeopteryx

Above: The family tree of the birds has many side branches. These illustrate the evolution of different genera and species to fill many niches. Throughout the Cainozoic, avifaunas were characterised by the appearance of more and more modern species. The evolution and dispersal of the large flightless birds is an important feature of the Pliocene-Pleistocene period.

Below: Some Upper Cretaceous birds. *Hesperornis,* which was 1 metre tall, was flightless and had teeth. The ichthyornids were about 20 cm tall and resembled modern terns.

Hesperornis

Icthyornids

Ichthyornids

Mammals

Millions of years passed before the mammals, which first appeared in the Triassic, became the dominant vertebrate animals. The various trends within the mammal-like reptiles, known as therapsids, culminated in the appearance of small, rather insignificant shrew-like mammals known as pantotheres. These included *Megazostrodon* and *Morganucodon* which are known from skulls, isolated teeth and partial skeletons. Early mammal teeth have distinctive cusp patterns and it is likely that the mammals possessed a high metabolic rate. They were insectivores and nocturnal.

Marsupial allantoic embryo

Placental embryo

Above: **Embryos of marsupial and placental mammals exhibit basic differences that reflect the evolutionary status of the two groups. The placenta enables the embryo mammal to remain longer in the womb and develop to a more advanced state** before birth. For example, an adult cat and opossum are very similar in size and weight, but the gestation period of the (marsupial) opossum is 13 days, whereas that of the (placental) cat is 60 days.

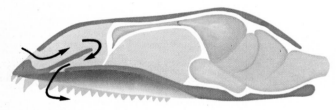

There are several basic differences in the skull structure of reptiles and mammals. In a reptile (above) the air passes through the nose into the front of the mouth, and the cerebral hemispheres are small. In mammals (below) the air passes into the back of the mouth and the cerebral hemispheres are very large. The dentition in mammals is also more complex.

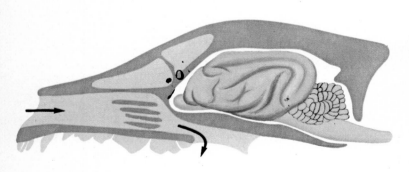

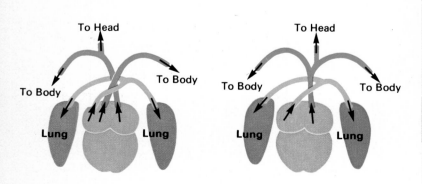

In chelonians and diapsids the main vessel which supplies blood to the head and body has split into right and left portions (*left*). Whereas in mammals, and presumably their synapsid ancestors, this split has not taken place.

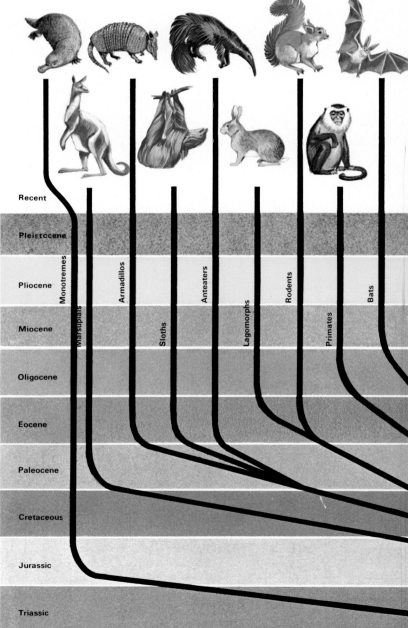

reconstruction of a pantothere

Opossum

The evolution of the mammals. Adaptive radiation of the mammals reached a climax in the Pliocene, with a greater variety of advanced, specialised mammals than ever before or since.

The pantotheres are among the earliest mammals, superficially they may have resembled the marsupial opossum or even mice and rats.

The record of mammalian families during the Jurassic and for much of the Cretaceous is a poor one. Few mammals grew beyond the size of a domestic cat and they presented no challenge to the various dinosaurs. By the end of the Cretaceous the primitive forms were joined by representatives of the marsupials and placentals. The marsupials and placentals are similar in many ways: they have larger brains than their synapsid cousins, secondary palates and a refined circulatory system. Unlike placentals however, the marsupial embryo leaves the womb in a very underdeveloped state and crawls into the mother's pouch to suckle and grow. Placental embryos undergo a long gestation period inside the body and are often born with most of their faculties, ready to function; for example the young of herding animals are capable of keeping up with their parents soon after they have risen from the ground and taken their first faltering steps. The placentals are the most advanced of all animals and it is their success that warrants the application of the term the 'Age of Mammals' to the Tertiary Period. The first marsupials were the ancestors of the living opossums and kangaroos but their success was limited as a result of direct competition with the more advanced placental stocks. They flourished briefly on several continents but were gradually forced to retreat into southern South America and Australia. Continental drift separated the marsupials of Australia from the 'mainland' areas and allowed an essentially primitive group to diversify and fill many ecological niches.

Medium to large placental mammals first appeared approximately 60 million years ago. They included the first carnivores and primates and slightly later were joined by the first horses and other ancestral ungulates (hoofed mammals). By the Upper Eocene the horses were well established and the first mammals had returned to an aquatic mode of life. These were the giant primitive whales such as *Basilosaurus*, representatives of which grew to over 18 metres in length.

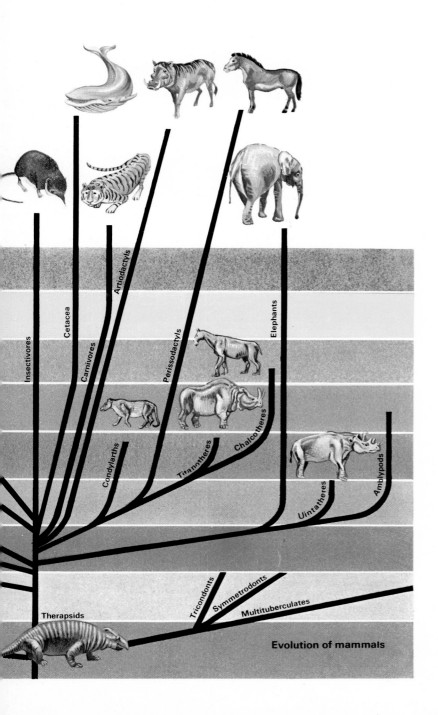

Insectivores
Cetacea
Carnivores
Artiodactyls
Perissodactyls
Elephants
Condylarths
Titanotheres
Chalcotheres
Uintatheres
Amblypods
Triconodonts
Symmetrodonts
Multituberculates
Therapsids

Evolution of mammals

Mammals

Thylacosmilus (left)
and Borhyaena (right)

Machairodus, the sabre-toothed tiger

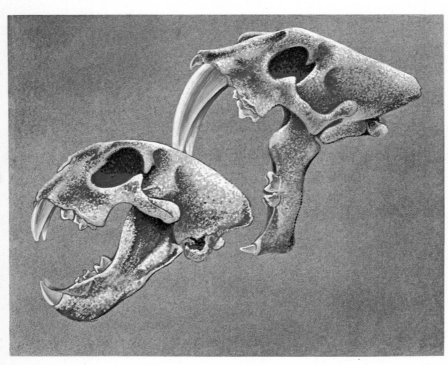

Amongst the carnivores, 'modern' forms succeeded the primitive creodonts and miacids in early Oligocene times. Civets, hyaenas, cats and dogs were represented in Oligocene faunas, whilst badgers and bears appeared in the Miocene. Of the cats, the sabre-toothed tigers are most impressive, their huge canines being used to stab and slice their prey. *Smilodon* and *Machairodus* were successful predators and the pattern of success was strangely paralleled amongst the marsupials by *Thylacosmilus.* It is assumed that the sabre-toothed cats fed on thick-skinned herbivores; their huge teeth, wide jaw gape and powerful build enabling them to pounce and kill their victim quickly and efficiently.

Another example of convergence occurs between the horses and the horse-like litopterns of South America. This

Marsupials and placentals alike adopted a sabre-toothed dentition. *Thylacosmilus* (here shown with the smaller, wolfish marsupial *Borhyaena* from the Miocene) and other marsupial 'cats' flourished during the Pliocene in South America and Australia. At the same time and also in the Pleistocene, placental sabre-toothed 'cats' such as *Machairodus* ruled North America and the Old World. It is probable that both groups killed their prey with a downward stabbing action.

Right: The evolution of the horse is among more detailed stories of the Cainozoic. Various changes mark the adaptation to a grass-eating mode of life on the open plains.

Left: Skull of a Sabre-toothed Tiger (above) compared to that of a modern cat (left) to show modifications for striking and biting.

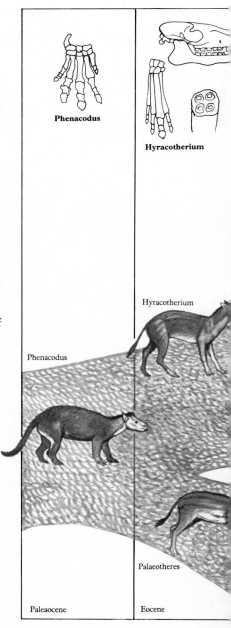

Phenacodus

Hyracotherium

Hyracotherium

Phenacodus

Palaeotheres

Paleaocene

Eocene

phenomenon of similar appearance between isolated species occurs when animals become adapted to the same basic mode of life. *Thoatherium* from the Miocene of South America was the same size as its horse equivalent *Mesohippus* and superficially they are similar. *Thoatherium* is a 'pseudohorse' however, as its teeth are lower crowned and its single-toed limbs are more reduced. The evolutionary history of the horse is amongst the best documented in the fossil record. Several mammalian stocks provide excellent data on various evolutionary processes. The rodents often exhibit miniscule changes and some scientists believe they are good indicators of gradual change. The same has been said for the horses and elephants but amongst these groups the differences between animals may represent major and abrupt changes in the direction of evolution. This is termed punctuated equilibrium and it may be indicative of a more powerful mechanism for change and adaptation.

The tooth of *Deinotherium*, a member of the early elephant-like mammals. This animal, which had tusks on the lower jaw, was found from the Lower Miocene to the Middle Pleistocene.

The teeth of *Equus*, as shown here, are very high crowned with the upper crowns having a square outline and the lower crowns a rectangular one. Both have a complex pattern.

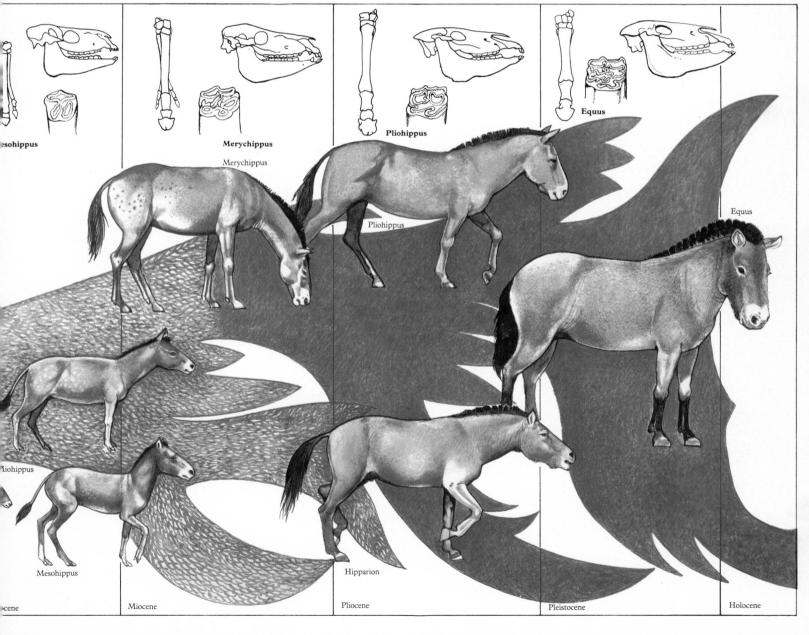

Mesohippus

Merychippus

Pliohippus

Equus

Merychippus

Pliohippus

Equus

Mesohippus

Hipparion

...iohippus

...cene

Miocene

Pliocene

Pleistocene

Holocene

Primates including Man

Mankind's ancestry is well documented and its evolution since the Pliocene is a tale of considerable success. The first primates appeared in the Palaeocene, 65 million years ago. *Plesiadapis* was a four-legged tree dweller. It had a long snout, clawed hands and a bushy tail. It is known from England, France and North America and is thought to be the transitional form between the primates and primitive insectivores. Various characters suggest that it is also ancestral to lemurs, tarsiers, monkeys, apes and even man.

Geographically, the higher primates can be divided into the South American monkeys and the Old World monkeys, apes and hominids. Of these, the New World genera are the more primitive with the howling monkeys and the capuchins being the best known examples. Their ancestors first appeared in the Upper Eocene, slightly earlier than their Old World cousins.

During the Oligocene, *Propliopithecus* represented the ancestral apes, whereas *Oligopithecus* and *Aegyptopithecus* were more advanced and probably the precursors of the 'oak-apes' or dryopithecines. *Dryopithecus* or 'Proconsul' was rather small with a rounded face and anthropoid characteristics. It had short arms

Above: **Oreopithecus was the size of a chimpanzee and lived in the swamplands of Lower Pliocene Italy. It had an erect or semi-erect posture, and its long arms were ideal for movement through trees. It was not, however, a direct ancestor of Man.**

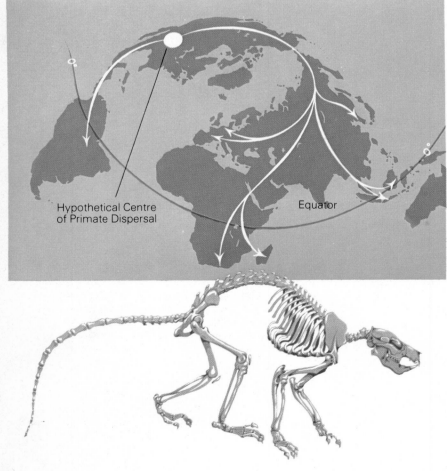

The early prosimians dispersed outwards from North America. This is probably true of the earliest known primate *Plesiadapis* (above) which is known from North America and Europe.

Structural Groups	Taxonomic Groups	Anatomical Features
Modern sapiens	*Homo sapiens sapiens*	Modern teeth and jaws; chins present. Large brains (Range 1,000–2,000 cc., mean 1,300 cc.). Striding bipedalism. Power and precision grips. (Stone, bone and later metal tools, use of fire)
	Homo sapiens neanderthalensis	Less modern teeth; no chins present. Large brains (Range 1,200–1,600 cc.). Good bipedalism. Power grip, perhaps precision grip. (Stone tools only, use of fire)
Late human phase	*Homo erectus*	Less advanced, larger teeth; no chins. Smaller brains (Range 750–1,200 cc.). Probably good bipedalism. Grip not known. (Crude stone tools, use of fire)
Early human phase	*Homo habilis*	Less advanced, larger teeth; no chins. Small brains (Approximately 670 cc.). Advanced bipedalism. Power grip. (Early stone tool makers)
Pre-human phase	*Australopithecus africanus*	Hominid dentition. Very small brains (500 cc.). Early bipedalism. Grip not known. (Tool users, possibly early tool makers)
Early hominids	*Ramapithecus punjabicus* *Kenyapithecus wickerii* *Kenyapithecus africanus (?)*	Hominid dental features, nothing else known

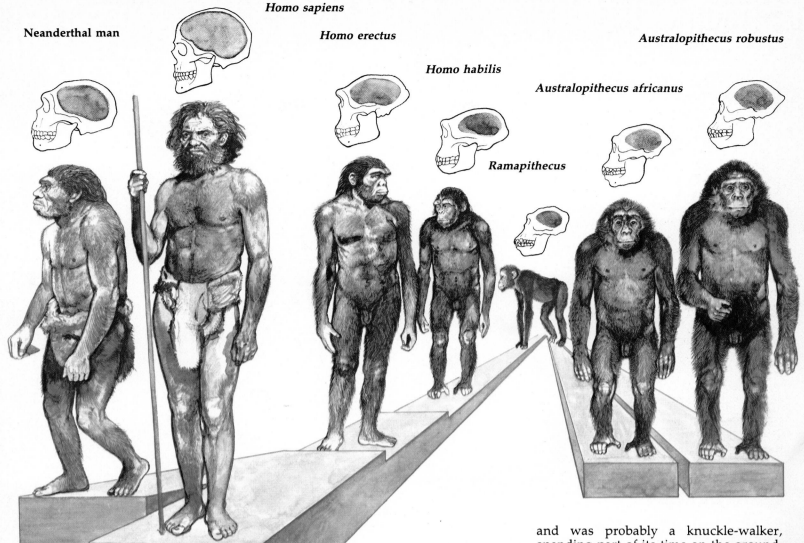

Neanderthal man

Homo sapiens

Homo erectus

Homo habilis

Australopithecus robustus

Australopithecus africanus

Ramapithecus

Above: **The evolution of modern man,**
***Homo sapiens,* is a controversial subject.**
This representation indicates that the
australopithecines were a side-branch
directly descended from *Ramapithecus*.

Hand tools including the most simple flint
chips and sophisticated polished hand
axes illustrate the development of Man as
a hunter and a craftsman. Initially
artefacts were used for defence, but were
then used in hunting and butchering prey.

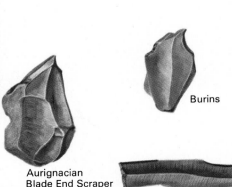

Chattelperonian Point

Aurignacian
Blade End Scraper

Burins

Late Paleolithic stone tools

and was probably a knuckle-walker,
spending part of its time on the ground.
After the dryopithecines, the evolutionary lines of man and the higher apes di-
verged. *Ramapithecus* is now regarded as
the ancestral or transitional genus to the
australopithecines and the hominids.
The australopithecines lived in Africa between 1 and 4 million years ago. They
were no more than 1.5 metres tall but,
significantly, were bipedal and of upright
stance: *Australopithecus africanus* was
more slender and gracile than *A. robustus*. The australopithecines may represent a side-branch in the evolution of
man with the true hominids being directly descended from *Ramapithecus*. Real
men appeared approximately 1.75 million years ago. *Homo habilis*, the 'handy-
man', was the first hominid to use
rudimentary tools and to build shelters.
For part of his life on Earth he co-existed
with both the australopithecines and
Homo erectus. Homo erectus, the 'erect-
man', was a hunter of big-game and his
tools were more sophisticated than his
contemporary. Between 250 000 and
500 000 years ago *Homo sapiens* appeared.
During the glacial periods, the neander-
thals (*Homo sapiens neanderthalis*) occupied areas of Europe and Asia and their
ability to adapt and migrate marked a
new departure in man's evolution. Some
35 000 years ago modern man (*Home sapiens sapiens*) emerged. Today man effectively controls his destiny, he is a
polluter, and a cause of extinction. He is
also creative and belatedly a
conservationist.

Prehistoric communities

The time that has elapsed since the formation of the Earth is unequally divided into the Precambrian eon (4000+ million years ago – 570 million years ago) and the Phanerozoic eon (570 million years ago – present day).

Precambrian rocks are known from all the major continents of the world. These rocks have often been altered by heat and pressure, produced by the numerous episodes of folding and emplacement of magmas.

Originally, the Precambrian was thought to be devoid of life and any unfossiliferous rocks underlying provable Cambrian rocks were called Precambrian. However, evidence of simple organisms has now been found within the Precambrian, along with the traces made by organisms moving upon and through the originally soft sediments.

The Phanerozoic ('obvious life') eon is the time of diversification within animals and plants, and saw widespread changes in the position and shape of the continental masses. Climatic change (often severe), sea-level changes and periods of mountain building came and went. This eon is divided into three eras, namely the Palaeozoic, Mesozoic and Cainozoic, which are themselves variably divided into periods (e.g., the Cambrian period).

The Palaeozoic era is heralded by the geologically 'sudden' appearance of several advanced invertebrate groups. During this era, all the major invertebrate phyla became established, as did terrestrial plants, fish, amphibians and reptiles. The close of the era is marked by mass extinctions throughout the animal and plant kingdoms, possibly due to marine regressions and climatic changes.

The Mesozoic era is best known as the time when dinosaurs proliferated, although invertebrate and plant stocks rediversified following earlier extinctions. Mammals also became established. Like the Palaeozoic era, the end of this era is distinguished by mass extinctions which affected marine and terrestrial organisms alike, including the dinosaurs. What caused these extinctions? Even now, we are not really sure.

The Cainozoic era is called the 'Age of Mammals'. Not only mammals but also flowering plants (angiosperms) and birds flourished, whilst new invertebrate families evolved. The latter part of the era witnessed the evolution and development of a mammal called man.

Cambrian

Colonial organisms such as *Charnia* are found in Precambrian rocks in Great Britain.

Fossil jellyfishes including *Medusina* were well represented over 600 million years ago.

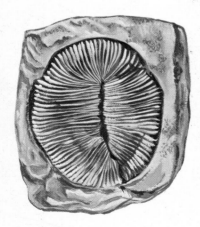

The first worms probably appeared over 650 million years ago. They were the ancestors of many advanced groups of animals.

The Cambrian Period (570–500 million years ago) is marked by the appearance of the first animals with mineralised hard parts. The period is the first of six that comprise the Palaeozoic Era (see table on p. 13) and is noted for the abundance of trilobites and several other groups of animals without backbones. At the beginning of the Cambrian shallow seas advanced over continental areas and many new ecological niches were developed. New groups of organisms evolved to fill these niches and adapt to new habitats, and unlike their supposed Precambrian ancestors, these organisms with their protective or supportive skeletons left a permanent record in the rocks of the Cambrian Period.

Strangely, animals such as the jointed-limbed trilobites were already very diverse in form by the beginning of the Cambrian. This suggests a long period of evolution beforehand, with ancestral stocks migrating throughout the seas of our planet. It is possible to use the trilobites as zone fossils for the

Any reconstruction of Cambrian life would be dominated by the presence of trilobites. In our panorama the importance of the early arthropods is fully recognised and an attempt is made to show that genera such as *Olenellus* and *Paradoxides* were restricted to specific sub-periods. Their association with other organisms is also important and in several areas of the world, palaeontologists can recognise the presence of recurrent associations or communities. In the Lower Cambrian, *Olenellus* and its relatives were common in northwest Scotland, Greenland, and parts of western Canada and the United States. This distribution is indicative of distinct communities, with *Olenellus* existing as a surface crawler.

Paradoxides is a Middle Cambrian trilobite, and its elongate genal spines and spiny tail are diagnostic characters. Some species grew to 30 cm in length. It is often found with the inarticulate brachiopod *Linguella* and the gastropod-like *Hyolithes*. This group of animals lived in marine shallow-water environments.

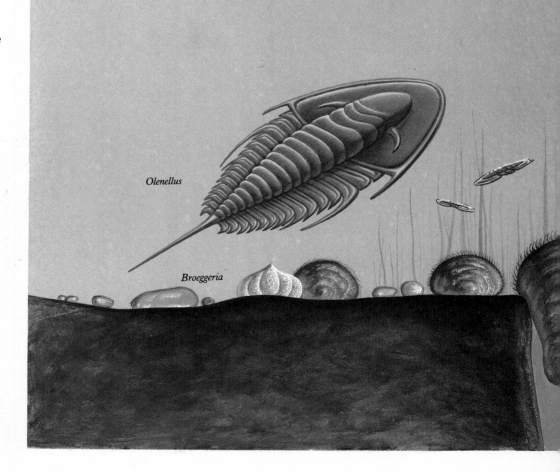

Cambrian period and to recognise that various groups occurred in distinct faunal provinces. Many trilobites dwelt on or in the sediments of the sea floor and were mostly scavengers or mud grubbers. Other forms were active swimmers or floaters and perhaps predatory.

Sea snails, brachiopods and the sponge-like archaeocyathids co-existed with the trilobites in many Cambrian communities. During the Middle Cambrian evidence for the presence of a strange, extremely varied fauna was preserved in the muddy sediments of the Burgess Shales of British Columbia, Canada. Worms, brachiopods, sponges and algae are all recorded in beautiful detail but amongst the most spectacular fossils are arthropods such as *Marrella, Burgessia* and *Opabinia*. Like the trilobites, these animals have jointed limbs with attached gill branches. Their shapes are more exotic than those of their distant cousins however, and the majority were probably free-swimming forms. Associated with these and other animals of the Burgess Shales are the bizarre animals *Halluci-genia* and *Canadia*. Of the two, *Canadia* is probably a polychaete worm, but *Hallucigenia* is unlike any known animal. It possessed a worm-like body with a rounded head whilst on its back it had seven tentacles and it walked on seven pairs of stilt-like limbs.

Agnostus is a representative of a diminutive family of trilobites that lived during the Cambrian and Ordovician.

Dictyonema

Ctenopyge

Paradoxides

Peltura

Agnostus

Bellerophon

Billingsella

Lingulella

Ordovician

Of the major groups present during the Cambrian, only the archaeocyathids are not found in the Ordovician Period (500–435 million years ago). Perhaps a modest ecological crisis took place during the Cambrian with new groups evolving to replace them as reef builders.

In the Northern Hemisphere, parts of what are now Europe and North America were separated by a major ocean – the Iapetus. Along its shorelines, new communities flourished whilst in the open oceanic waters planktonic and free-swimming animals were abundant. The shallow water communities were dominated by trilobites and brachiopods. Many Ordovician trilobites belonged to the blind trinucleid stock and were adapted to mud-grubbing or filter-feeding modes of life. Certain Ordovician trilobites, unlike their Cambrian forebears, could also tuck their tail areas beneath their bodies for protection. Some forms even developed a tooth and socket locking system with the underside of the head and tail able to become firmly secured together to protect against likely predators.

Brachiopods, the most common sea shells of the Palaeozoic, varied considerably in the Ordovician. New genera evolved to fill both shallow and deep water niches, with a complex, filament-covered, food-gathering organ efficiently filtering water drawn into the bivalved shell. Shell shape, thickness and ornament are useful in determining the mode of life and environment of a given brachiopod. In shallow water environments, brachiopods coexisted with early corals, bryozoans and both stalked and free-living echinoderms. Of the fixed echinoderms, crinoids formed distinct gardens with their 'feather-like' arms efficiently filtering food currents. The arms were arranged as a vertical fan, with numerous small, tube-like soft parts forming the filter net.

In the Ordovician, the roles of major scavenger and carnivore were filled by the nautiloids. These distant relatives of the squid and octopus flourished in both shallow and deep water realms and some reached gigantic proportions. Their shells were chambered, which provided buoyancy control, and various shapes and internal deposits are indicators of different modes of life. In oceanic waters, some nautiloids might have fed on the rapidly evolving graptolites. The latter first appeared in the Cambrian but during the Ordovician their numbers and variety increased to such an extent that they are ideal zone fossils in many parts of the world.

Right: **Phyllograptus elongatus, a 'leaf-like' graptolite from Lower Ordovician Norway. 1·8 cm long.**

Below: **Trilobites such as *Tretaspis sortita* (Upper Ordovician Scotland) were blind, sea-floor dwellers. 3·3 cm long.**

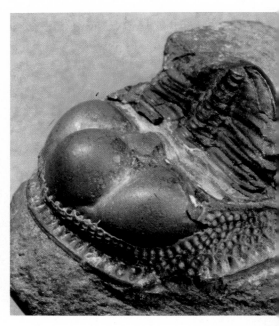

A flat-bottom marine environment in the Ordovician. The organisms include *Dalmanella* and *Orthambonites* (orthid brachiopods); *Lonchodomus*, *Merlinia* and *Remopleurides* (trilobites); *Lophospira* (gastropod) and nautiloids as well as many crinoids (sea-lilies).

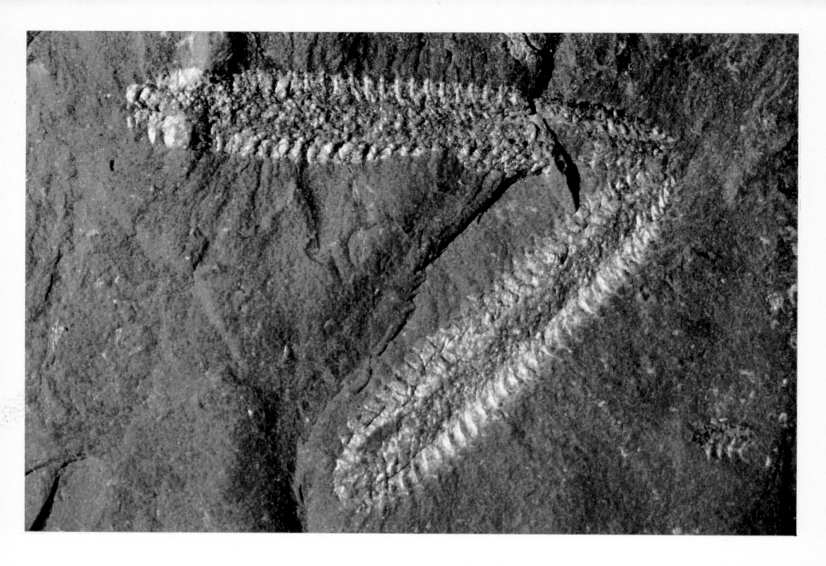

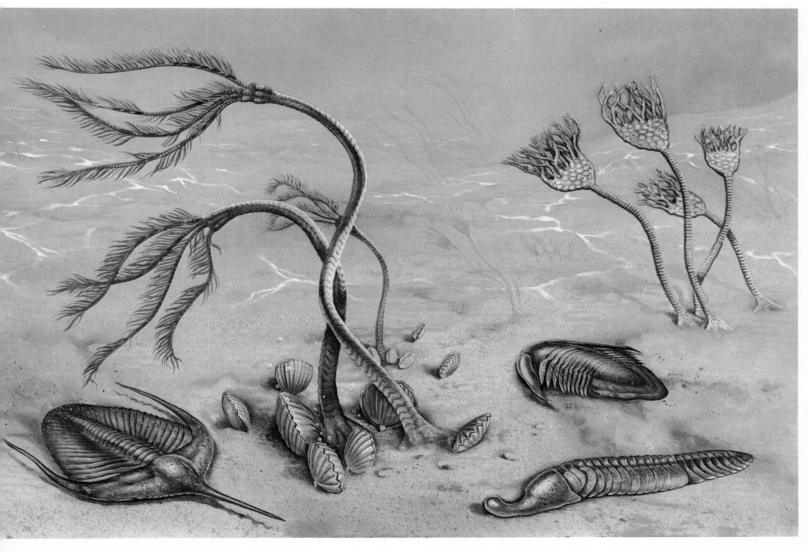

Silurian

The Silurian Period (435–395 million years ago) is sub-divided into series and zones on the basis of graptolites, brachiopods and rock types: shales and limestones are common.

Geologists recognise two main faunas. The first existed in shallow waters and was composed of brachiopods, corals, bryozoans and crinoids. It is often termed the 'shelly fauna' or facies and is best studied in the limestone of the Wenlock series. Blocks of limestone covered in thousands of fossils represent the ancient sea floor, and are often preserved *in situ*. A reconstruction of the community based on both fossil content and enclosing sediment indicates that the animals lived in warm, shallow waters as reef dwellers; within the community brachiopods such as *Leptaena* and *Atrypa* were common.

In contrast to the abundance of organisms present in the Wenlock Limestone, inshore and deeper-water brachiopod-dominated communities had a restricted variety of animal life.

Beyond the brachiopod or shelly communities, in still deeper water, lay muds and numerous graptolites. The sediments were deposited beyond the continental shelf and on a poorly oxygenated sea floor. Graptolites floated as plankton in the surface waters and on death drifted to the sea floor; the single-branched *Monograptus triangulatus* and *Rastrites maximus* are typically Silurian.

Right: **Bone beds such as the Ludlow Bone Bed shown here, may accumulate remains over a considerable period of time.**

Below: **Reef-building and reef-dwelling organisms flourished in the Silurian. Beautiful fossils are often found covering the surfaces of rocks that were once the sea floor.**

Bottom: **The richly fossiliferous bedding planes of the Wenlock Limestone (Silurian) allow reconstructions of the environment.**

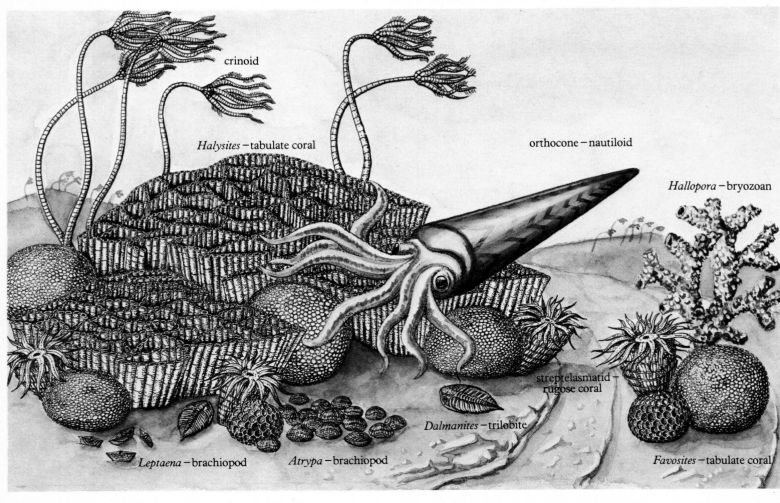

crinoid

Halysites – tabulate coral

orthocone – nautiloid

Hallopora – bryozoan

streptelasmatid – rugose coral

Dalmanites – trilobite

Leptaena – brachiopod

Atrypa – brachiopod

Favosites – tabulate coral

Primitive land plants and animals also appeared in the late Silurian. The plants were similar to the existing *Psilotum* and needed a wet substrate to survive. *Palaeophonus*, a scorpion, was possibly the first terrestrial animal: it had a tough mineralised skeleton and was well adapted to the rigours of its new environment. In fresh waters new forms of fishes, derived from *Anatolepis* in the early Ordovician, flourished. Their main enemies were the eurypterids, distant relatives of *Palaeophonus*. They, too, were jointed-limbed, but their segmented bodies could grow to over 1·8 metres in length. By the end of the Silurian, terrestrial plants and animals were well-established and able to exploit new conditions in the Devonian.

Monograptus was a single-stiped graptoloid. As these colonial animals were widespread but short-lived they are often used in sediment zonation.

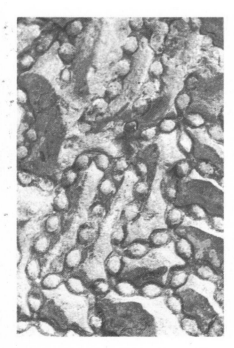

Frequently called the 'chain coral', *Halysites* consists of a number of linked elongate corallites.

Above: **Eurypterus lacustris (Silurian, Buffalo, USA)** and its eurypterid brethren are often called the giant water scorpions. 14·5 cm long.

Below: Eurypterids grew up to 2 metres long and lived in estuaries and lagoons. They are often found with agnathid fish and it is possible that the giant arthropods hunted and killed the smaller, defenceless vertebrates.

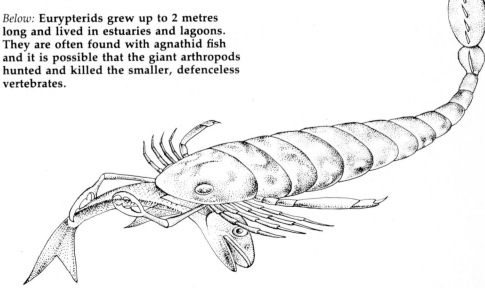

63

Devonian

For much of the Devonian Period (395–345 million years ago) a major continental landmass existed in the Northern Hemisphere. Around its shorelines, reefs and shelly faunas flourished whilst beyond in deeper water brachiopods and goniatites were abundant. On land, reed-bed deposits indicate an essentially arid environment with localised swamps covered with plants of the earliest true floras. Amongst these were the earliest vascular plants including *Rhynia* and *Asteroxylon*. *Rhynia* was a primitive psilopsid which grew to approximately 20cms in height. *Asteroxylon*, an early lycopod, had a well defined star-shaped arrangement of its vascular tissues within the stem and tightly packed leaflets over the stem. Within the swamp waters and sediments, small arthropods lived as parasites.

Fishes became so common and varied during the Devonian that the period is often referred to as the Age of Fishes. At first heavily armoured forms such as *Cephalaspis*, *Coccosteus* and *Bothriolepis* were dominant but by the end sharks, lungfishes and ray-finned bony fishes were most common. The lungfishes belong to the 'tassel-finned' fishes as does the coelocanth. From this group came the ancestors of the first amphibian, *Ichthyostega* which existed in the Upper Devonian.

In the seas of the Devonian period, brachiopods, corals, bryozoans and crinoids were numerous in reef communities. In deeper water shales, the faunas were more restricted with elongate spiriferide brachiopods and free-swimming goniatites as the most common faunal elements. The muddy limestones of the Devonian have yielded numerous tooth-like structures called conodonts. These have been associated with many animals but are still a mystery. At the end of the Devonian, new plants and animals had begun to give our planet a green cover and a more familiar community structure.

Above: Hexagonaria, **was a widespread massive coral that occurred during the Devonian.**
Below: **The tooth-like fossil of a conodont, the origin of these fossils is uncertain.**

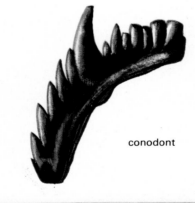

conodont

Below: **The red coloration and angled stratification of sandstones in both the Devonian and Permo-Triassic Periods indicate a terrestrial environment.**

Cyrtospirifer **is a member of the group of brachiopods which are used as zone fossils for the Devonian period.**

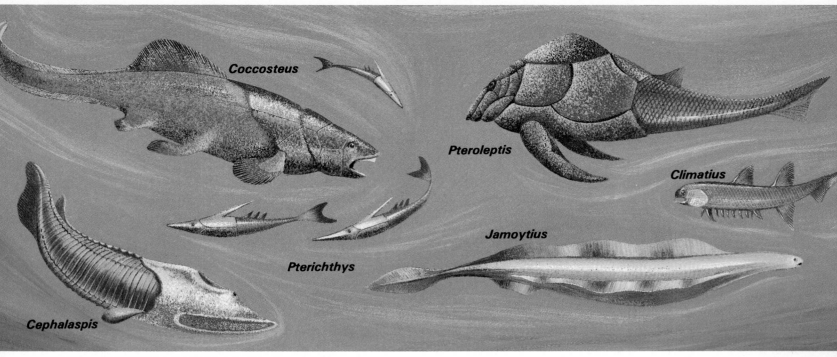

Coccosteus

Pteroleptis

Climatius

Jamoytius

Pterichthys

Cephalaspis

Above: The Devonian is also known as the Age of Fishes. Those illustrated represent a few of the forms that were common.
Below: The major landmass of the Devonian. Existing continents are outlines, red spots mark the major fossil sites.
Bottom and right: **Ichthyostega**, the first amphibian.

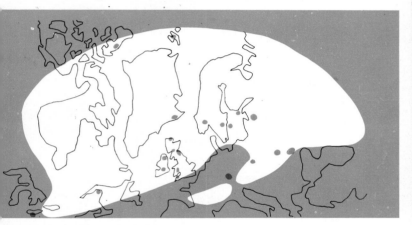

Carboniferous

The Carboniferous Period lasted from 345 to 280 million years ago, and North American geologists divide it into two systems: the Pennsylvanian and the Mississippian. The early or Lower Carboniferous (Mississippian) is noted for the presence of shallow, warm seas over large areas of the Northern Hemisphere. Corals and brachiopods were numerous and reefs composed of a variety of rugose corals are recorded from many countries. *Lithostrotion* is an example of the colonial corals of this time, whilst *Canina* is an example of the large solitary corals that existed. The profusion of reef life and the large size of many fossils indicates that the warm waters and abundant food and

oxygen were ideal conditions. Amongst the brachiopods, the productids were now the dominant stock. These animals rested like giant clams on the sea floor whilst other genera, with elongate spines, were adapted to higher energy environments.

Approximately 325 million years ago the seas of the Lower Carboniferous began to recede to be replaced by swamps and vast forests with gigantic 'scale trees' such as *Lepidodendron* and horsetails such as *Calamites* and *Sphenophyllum*. In these swamplands the plentiful coal reserves of many countries accumulated; they were frequently flooded by river or sea waters and the fossil plants alternate with non-

marine bivalves and marine goniatites. These organisms and the corals of the Lower Carboniferous are used to provide relative ages for the deposits.

Within the warm, humid swamplands of the Upper Carboniferous (Pennsylvanian), amphibians thrived and diversified. Large aquatic genera included *Eogyrinus*, a predator which grew to over 4·5 metres. Other large forms were *Loxomma* and *Megalocephalus*. Smaller, specialised amphibians included *Ophiderpeton*, *Sauropleura* and *Microbrachis*. Of these, *Ophiderpeton* was snake-like whilst *Sauropleura* retained very reduced limbs. In *Microbrachis* the small limbs were well formed but with only three digits on each hand.

A reconstruction of the swampland forests of the Carboniferous.

Sphenophyllum, a horsetail, in which the leaves were carried in whorls. The smaller horsetails filled a niche similar to that occupied by the modern day rushes.

Eogyrinus, was a large, rather primitive amphibian that flourished in the waters of the swamps. Individuals attained lengths of up to 4.5 metres. *Eogyrinus* had a long fish-like tail and rather short limbs.

Meganeura, a giant flying insect which closely resembles the living dragonflies.

Cordaites, ancestrial to the true conifer.

an early arachnid

Hylonomus, a small captorhinomorph reptile.

Lithostrotion, a widespread Carboniferous coral which grew in shallow-water environments.

Productus, is a medium to large brachiopod which can be found in limestones of the Lower Carboniferous series in Europe and Asia.

Anthraconauta is an important non-marine member of the bivalve Myalmidae, a group of Carboniferous freshwater mussels.

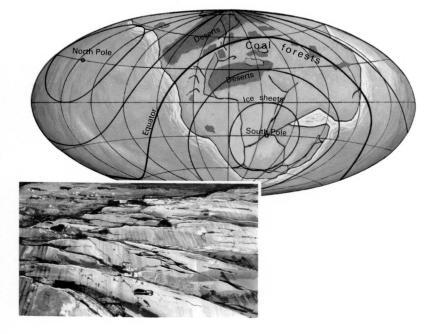

Left: Climatic belts in Carboniferous times before the split of Pangaea. *Inset* Glaciated pavements formed in India at this time, contrast with the warmer, swampy conditions that prevailed in Europe and North America.

A series of sedimentary units from the Coral Measures and their interpretation.

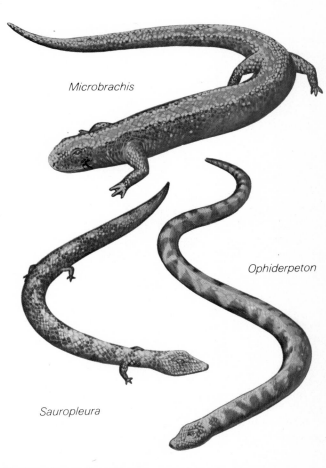

Microbrachis

Ophiderpeton

Sauropleura

	SEDIMENTS	FOSSILS	ENVIRONMENTS
	coal	leaves, stems, and spores of trees	swampy forests
	seat earth	roots	
	mudstone		surface built up to water level
	sandstone locally cross-bedded with irregularities		deltaic
			influx of river sands
	siltstone	plant debris	deltaic lagoons
	mudstone and shale		delta front or estuarine
	with ironstone nodules	mussels, fish	brackish water
	mudstone	marine molluscs	inundation by the sea
	coal		swampy forests

During the Carboniferous, numerous short-lived and highly adapted amphibians flourished in swamp and lake environments.

Permian

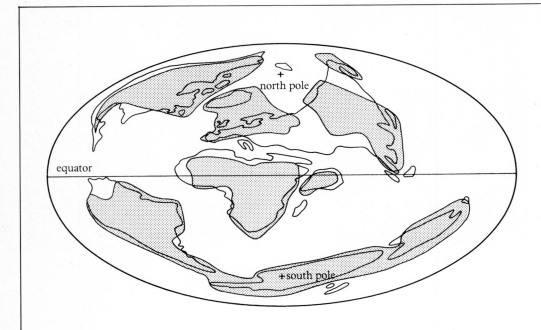

The paleographic reconstruction of the Permian world shows the presence of the supercontinent Pangaea, originally named by Alfred Wegener in 1915. The coming together of the continental masses caused a deepening of the oceans and a withdrawal of the shallow marine seas from the continental margins. As a result, the Permian terrestrial climates were more severe than those of earlier periods. Mass extinctions were the result of both marine regression and climatic change.

In the Permian Period (280–225 million years ago) the continents were fused into a huge land mass called Pangaea. The creation of one 'super-continent' led to climatic changes and reduced the area of continental shelf covered by shallow seas. As a result, the marine faunas of the Permian were restricted and numerous important groups of Palaeozoic organisms became extinct, including the rugose and tabulate stony corals, the trilobites, goniatites and many brachiopod families. In parts of North America and Asia, there developed the fusulinids, relatively large marine protozoans of the Order Foraminiferida, which played an important role as rock formers in western and central North America.

On land, climatic conditions affected the distribution of plants and animals: cold, wetland forests were present over large areas. Around the equator a Euramerican flora characterised by conifers, such as *Walchia* and seed ferns such as *Callipteris*, dominated. The Permian witnessed the demise of the ancient Carboniferous floras and the development of new plants which were to give a widespread, relative uniformity to the Triassic and Jurassic.

Towards the end of the Permian more arid conditions prevailed in many areas and as a result terrestrial faunas were eventually dominated by the reptiles. In the Lower Permian sail-backed reptiles such as *Dimetrodon* and *Edaphosaurus* dominated the food chains. Later their descendants, the mammal-like reptiles, assumed the dominant roles. These animals included the dog-toothed cynodonts, which in the form of *Cynognathus* filled the role of major predators until the early Triassic. By the end of the Permian the reptiles were supreme with new groups such as the lizards on land and the mesosaurs at sea.

Eryops grew to 1·75 metres in length. It was a fish-eater, roaming the swamp margins.

Cumbersome herbivorous reptiles like *Ophiacodon* became extinct during the Cretaceous.

Triassic

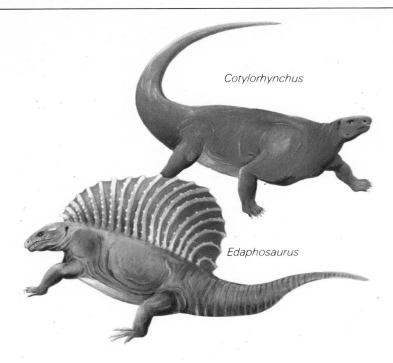

Cotylorhynchus

Edaphosaurus

Edaphosaurus was a pelycosaur with
powerful jaws adapted to feeding on
shellfish. The large sail-like membrane
was used to control body temperature.

**The bulky *Cotylorhynchus* was an
unsuccessful herbivorous pelycosaur of
the Lower Permian.**

At the start of the Triassic Period (225–
193 million years ago), the mammal-like
reptiles ruled most vertebrate communities, but the earliest archosaurs, the thecodontians, had begun to appear. At
first they were clumsy sprawling
animals, but gradually new and more efficient forms arose. The thecodontians included both quadrupedal and bipedal
animals and were savage efficient predators who were the direct ancestors of
the dinosaurs. They replaced the
mammal-like reptiles in the Middle Triassic, but by the Late Triassic they too were
challenged as the first dinosaurs which
had appeared in South Africa and South
America had spread northwards into
North America and Europe.

Throughout the Triassic, the niches va-
cated by the now extinct organisms of
the Palaeozoic were filled by new groups.
In the marine realm, the goniatites were
replaced by the ceratites and eventually
by the ammonites, whilst many brachiopod niches were occupied by the rapidly
evolving bivalves. New corals, bryozoans
and echinoderms also appeared in the
Triassic seas. The increase in marine invertebrates was matched by an increased
diversification amongst the bony fishes
and the return of reptiles in the form of
the ichthyosaurs and plesiosaurs to an
aquatic life.

Bauria (above) and Thrinaxodon (below)

Above: **Numerous changes to their
skeletons and soft parts gave the mammal-
like reptiles an advanced appearance.**

Morganucodon

Above: **Small mammals such as *Morganucodon* first
appeared in the Triassic.**

Gryphaea are frequently referred to as
'Devil's toenails' due to the form of the
Triassic mollusc's unequal valves. The
very broad shells suggest that some
species were adapted to live on soft muds.

Jurassic

The Jurassic Period (193–136 million years ago) is the second of the three periods of the Mesozoic Era. The two major continents then existing were at first linked together as Pangaea, but during the early Jurassic they became separated by the equatorial Tethys Ocean. Shallow shelf seas covered most of Europe and the invertebrate stocks that first appeared during the Triassic now flourished. Bivalves were numerous in most shallow or relatively shallow water environments and a variety could be distinguished: for example, *Gryphaea*, the

'Devil's-toenail', was a mud reclining bivalve, whilst relatives of the living oyster cemented themselves to the rocks of the sea-floor. Echinoderms, crinoids and corals were also common. The crinoids formed distinct 'gardens' whilst corals such as *Isastraea* played an important role in the building of reefs. Brachiopods such as *Terebratula* and *Goniorhynchia* were abundant in the shallow margins of the warm Jurassic seas.

In deeper waters, the ammonites were now distributed throughout the world; numerous species are used both as zone fossils and to provide a relative time scale for the Jurassic Period. Ichthyosaurs and plesiosaurs were the major predators of the Jurassic seas.

On land the dinosaurs were now firmly established as the ruling reptiles. Plated dinosaurs such as *Stegosaurus*

were important members of several vertebrate communities, whilst the role of major predator or meat-eater was assumed by various members of the *Megalosaurus-Allosaurus* group. Small dinosaurs including *Campsognathus* were present in numbers and from such a coelurosaurian ancestor arose *Archaeopteryx*, the first bird. The climate of the Jurassic was more equable than that of the Triassic and the gymnosperms, non-flowering plants, dominated the world's floras.

Plated dinosaurs such as *Stegosaurus* and passive iguanodonts co-existed in the Jurassic with large and small meat-eating theropods. *Apatosaurus* and *Brachiosaurus* were huge, plant-eating sauropods that have been found in several Upper Jurassic dinosaur communities. They lived in swampland areas, spending much of their life in water.

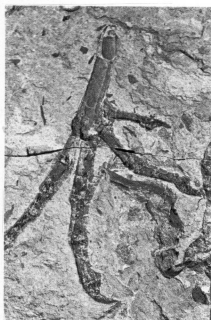

Goniorhynchia is a medium-sized rather wide rhynchonellid, a group of Jurassic brachiopods. This genus is often used as a zone fossil.

Stegosaurus

A fossil bird's foot. The remains of fossil birds are uncommon although the discoveries of *Archaeopteryx* in the Jurassic Lithographic stone of Bavaria are spectacular.

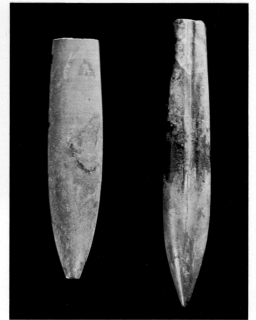

Above: **Isastrea** a Jurassic colonial coral. These corals are often found in association with various brachiopods and it is likely that they existed in shallow-water environments.

Above right: **Hibolites** is a representative of an extinct group of molluscs called the belemnites. These are the only common fossils of a class that is now represented by the squids and octopus.

Brachiosaurus

Apatosaurus

Camptosaurus

ratosaurus

Cretaceous

To many people the Cretaceous Period (136–65 million years ago) is known by the white chalk (Latin: *Creta*) of northwest Europe. Not all Cretaceous rocks are chalky, however, and the Lower Cretaceous is dominated by sands and clays over much of Western Europe; certain of these sediments mark the continued withdrawal of the shelf seas which began in the late Jurassic.

Ammonites are again plentiful and varied in the Cretaceous, with giant forms such as *Pachydiscus* occurring late in the period. Echinoids were also abundant and irregular forms which burrowed deep into the sediment were among the most common: *Conulus* and *Micraster* are

the best known Cretaceous echinoids. At specific horizons within the Cretaceous, sponges formed 'gardens' with calcareous or siliceous species providing important information on either shallow or deeper water environments. Microfossils were particularly abundant in the Upper Cretaceous with planktonic protozoans such as the globigerinids and calcareous algae of various coccolithophore families having a rock-forming role in the chalk seas.

During the Cretaceous, the dinosaurs were still the ruling terrestrial animals, although the giant sauropods were gradually replaced by various representatives of 'bird-hipped' families. The

Upper Cretaceous marked a rapid diversification of the ornithischians with numerous species of duck-billed or crested, horned and heavily armoured families living in herds in North America and Asia. Egg sites from North America and Asia indicate that the dinosaurs organised their nests with great care and may have protected their young, rather than abandoning them. It is likely that the parent animal fed on the lush plains, but moved into the lower hill slopes to lay

Below: **The Upper Cretaceous plains of North America supported a varied fauna of both meat and plant-eating dinosaurs.**

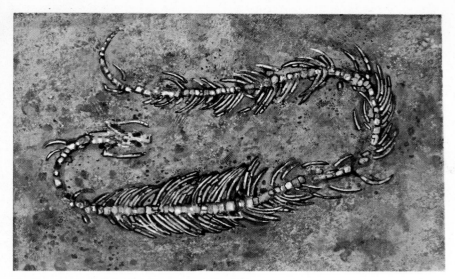

Snakes appeared in the Cretaceous Period and fossils such as this can sometimes be found.

Right: **Nannofossils such as *Cyclococcolithus floridanus* are extremely abundant in the chalk of Northern Europe. Such fossils are important in dating rocks.**

***Micraster* is an irregular echinoid from the Cretaceous-Palaeocene that can be found commonly in Europe. Some species are used as zone fossils.**

her eggs. *Tyrannosaurus rex* is the best known Cretaceous dinosaur, and was the chief predator and the largest meat-eater of all time. The smaller coelurosaurs were well adapted to the roles of scavenger or nest robber.

The floras of the early Cretaceous were rather similar to that of the Jurassic, but flowering plants became a very important component later on. Broad-leaved

***Conulus* is an echinoid that has a flat ventral surface with the main body having a hemispherical or conical form. This is a distinctive fossil abundant in the Upper Cretaceous chalk of Europe.**

plants were common, with cycads and ferns in the minority. Very recently, flowers similar to the living species *Vahlia capensis*, from southern Africa and Afghanistan, have been found in the Upper Cretaceous chalk deposits of Sweden.

In the seas, ichthyosaurs and plesiosaurs were less common than earlier. The major predators of the Upper Cretaceous were the mosasaurs with their huge jaws and elongate, streamlined bodies. Turtles were common and the giant *Archelon* grew to approximately 4 metres long.

At the end of the Cretaceous the mosasaurs, *Archelon*, the dinosaurs and many groups of invertebrates became extinct. The likely causes were probably related to continental drift and changes in the floras and climate, but it is possible that an extra-terrestrial happening such as the explosion of a supernova was a contributory factor in this mass extinction.

Anatosaurus

Saurolophus

Triceratops

Ornithomimus

Cainozoic

If the Mesozoic Era was the 'Age of the Dinosaurs', then the Cainozoic Era (65 million years ago onward) is the 'Age of Mammals'. It consists of the Palaeocene, Eocene, Oligocene, Miocene, Pliocene and Quaternary Periods. Since the Mesozoic, the continents had drifted apart and their positions were near to those of the present day. The Atlantic Ocean continued to widen whilst the equatorial Tethys Ocean was to close in the east as a result of the movements of Arabia and possibly India. Seasonality became more important as the era progressed and the foundations of migration were laid early on. These may have been triggered by the beginnings of the ice ages and the mountain building movements that climaxed, in Europe, in the building of the

Above: **Huge meat-eating birds such as *Diatryma* flourished during the Palaeocene (Lower Cainozoic) in North America and Europe.**

Although certain titanotheres looked like the living rhinoceros, they were members of a more primitive stock which first appeared in North America. A titanothere head is shown below.

Alps and, in North America, in the building of the Rockies.

Angiosperms continued to dominate world floras and more and more plants similar to living species evolved. From the Isle of Sheppey, south-east England, there is evidence that tropical palms similar to those of Malaysia flourished there. From Menat, central France, deposits of similar age have yielded traces of oak, elm, poplar and roses as well as redwoods, cypresses, yews and mushrooms. These outcrops are of Palaeocene–Eocene age and apart from plants, provide evidence of mammal and avian evolution.

Amongst the mammals of Sheppey and Menat are the earliest representatives of the horses (*Hyracotherium*), the primates (*Plesiadapis*) and hoofed animals (*Coryphodon*). The same or similar genera occur in North America and from these we can determine that an early radiation of animals had begun. The birds of the Paleocene include the gigantic 'terror-cranes' such as *Diatryma*, game birds, pigeons, herons, cuckoos and waders.

Throughout the Cainozoic, the mammalian and bird faunas were constantly evolving. Whales first appeared in the Eocene, closely followed by groups such as the sirenians: seals and walruses. Carnivorous mammals were first represented by the cat-like oxyaenids and miacids in the Cretaceous-Palaeocene, and these diversified in the Eocene and Oligocene with the evolution of the bears, cats, hyaenids and weasels. Dogs and sealions appear in the Miocene.

In the oceans of the world, molluscs in the form of bivalves and gastropods flourished, with only the nautiloids surviving of the numerous cephalopod families of the Mesozoic. Small invertebrates such as the foraminiferids were important as rock formers (*Nummulites*, *Alveolina*) whilst algal blooms and planktonic globigerinids thrived in open marine conditions. Crabs represent the arthropods in marine water.

Right: **The fossil of a beetle clearly showing the front wings and abdomen. This specimen was collected from the fine ash-rich sediments of Menat in Central France.**

A reconstruction of an Early Tertiary scene in central France. The opposum-like mammals are early primates, *Plesiadapis*.

Quaternary

The Quaternary is the last of the geological periods recognised by geologists: it began 1·5 million years ago and includes the present day. For much of the period, huge ice sheets covered most of North America, northwest Europe and Russia. The world was cooled by their presence and also sea levels fell approximately 90m (300ft). Fluctuations in the southward movement of the ice, together with climatic change, led to variations in the plant and animal communities. Periods of glaciation alternated with warm interglacials and different organisms adapted to the prevailing conditions thrived, albeit temporarily in some cases. Various techniques including the study of pollen distribution and oxygen-isotope ratios provide a clear insight into the climatic fluctuations. Pollen can be used to trace the change from tundra to a warmer mixed forest flora or vice versa, whilst oxygen-isotope ratios in the skeletons of deep water protozoans reflect sea level fluctuations and the build-up of land.

The evidence of change and evolution during the Quaternary is fossilized in various ways. In the Wiltshire district of Los Angeles, North America the Rancho la Brea tarpits have yielded, to careful collection, a late Pleistocene fauna of considerable interest. Evidence suggests that the prevailing climate changed from humid to one of warmer, more arid, conditions in 2000–3000 years. The nearby plains were stocked with herds of bison, horse and elephant, whereas the forest edges provided the ideal environment for the giant tree sloth. Strangely, most of the fossils are of carnivores, which suggests that they attended the pits in the expectancy of a large herbivore becoming stranded and helpless in the glue-like asphalt. Unwittingly, in their desire to feed they were also sucked into the pits.

The preservation of glacial communities is generally poorer than that of their warmer counterparts. River gravels do yield the teeth and bones of reindeer, bison and the huge mammoths that existed in these colder climes but detailed evidence is rare. Amongst the most spectacular finds are the mammoths from the north-eastern states of the Soviet Union, the complete bodies of which have been mummified under tundra conditions.

The changes in floras and faunas in the Quaternary are both intriguing and well documented. The development of Man is perhaps the most interesting, with the primitive hominids of the Pliocene giving rise to creative peoples who established settlements, utilised the resources that surrounded them and eventually began to control their environment. The Quaternary is the 'Age of Man' and the last 10 000 years have witnessed the progress of civilization.

A chart showing approximate correlations of glacial and interglacial terminology.

Pleistocene Glacial (blue) and Interglacial (red) Phases					Climate
Würm	Fourth		Late Wisconsian	Upper Pleistocene	
			Early Wisconsian		
Riss/Würm		Ipswichian	Sangamonian		
Riss	Third		Illinoian		
Mindel Riss		Hoxnian	Yarmouthian	Middle Pleistocene	
Mindel	Second		Kansanian		
Günz Mindel		Cromerian	Aftonian		
Günz	First		Nebraskan	Lower Pleistocene	
Alpine Names	Numerical Names	English Names	American Names	Major divisions of the Pleistocene	

Modern extent of the North Polar glaciation.

Below: **Pollen grains are useful indicators of climate and environment, and are important in the recognition of glacial and interglacial episodes.**

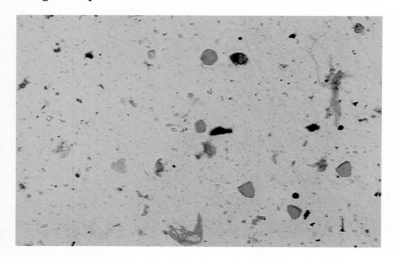

Maximum extent of the North Polar ice in the Würm glaciation during the Upper Pleistocene.

Right: Teeth of mammals reflect their feeding habits. For example, elephant teeth *(Elephas)* are robust and are used to crush and grind vegetation: hyaena teeth show it to be a carnivore.

Below: Cave drawings like tools and the use of fire, marked the continued evolution of Man. They record the animals that co-existed with our ancestors and are found throughout Europe and North Africa.

Bottom left: A Pleistocene glacial scene.

Bottom right: A Pleistocene interglacial scene.

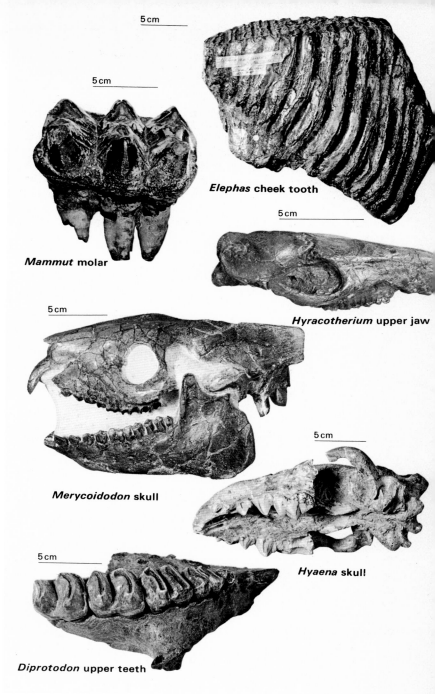

Elephas cheek tooth

Mammut molar

Hyracotherium upper jaw

Merycoidodon skull

Hyaena skull

Diprotodon upper teeth

Glossary

amber fossil resin

anaerobic bacteria minute organisms that exist in the absence of oxygen

anapsid a sub-class of reptile characterised by a skull roof in which the only openings are for the eyes and nostrils; living examples are the tortoises and turtles

angiosperm land plant with seeds in ovaries; any flowering plant

auricles wing-like growths of shell, in front and behind the beak (some scallops)

axial structure central structure in corallite (corals)

bituminous shale fine-grained sediment, rich in oil-like minerals

body fossil preserved remains of skeleton of soft parts of an organism

Cainozoic 65 million years onward: it comprises the Palaeocene, Eocene, Oligocene, Miocene, Pliocene, and Quaternary periods

Cambrian 570–500 million years ago

Carboniferous 345–280 million years ago

carbonisation fossilisation process in which only the carbon content of the organism is preserved

cartilage gristle-like substance forming a skeleton in some animals such as sharks and rays

cephalon head region of a trilobite

columella central column of shell in gastropods

coprolite fossilised faeces of an animal

coralite solitary coral or individual of colony

Cretaceous 136–65 million years ago

detritus feeder animal that feeds on organic matter coating grains of sediment or mixed with the sediment

Devonian 395–345 million years ago

diapsid a sub-class of reptile characterised by a skull roof with a pair of openings in addition to those for the eyes and nostrils

encrusting moss-like growth form (corals and bryozoans)

euryapsid a sub-class of reptile characterised by a skull roof with a single opening higher than that found in the synapsids in addition to those for the eyes and nostrils

external mould hardened sediment that shows the external features of an organism that has since been destroyed

facial suture paired grooves running from front to back on the heads of many trilobites

facies those assemblages of fossils, structures or minerals that indicate the environment of deposition of a particular sediment

faunal province large region containing numerous habitats that is isolated from other faunal provinces by some barrier to migration

filter feeder animal that feeds on organic matter suspended in seawater by creating a current through a feeding organ, which filters out the food

fossil any remains, impression or trace of a plant or animal from another geological period

Gondwanaland southern supercontinent comprising South America, Africa, India, Australia, New Zealand and Antarctica that existed in the Mesozoic

gymnosperm land plant with ovules not enclosed in ovaries, e.g. conifers

hemisessile describing any animal that spends part of its life in one spot but which may move in order to migrate or feed

hinge line region along which valves form a joint in bivalve molluscs and brachiopods

inarticulate describing a primitive class of brachiopods with no teeth

interglacial period warm time when ice sheets had retreated during Ice Ages

internal mould hardened sediment which shows the internal features of an organism (such as a clam) which has since been destroyed

involute the outer chambers of a shell overlapping those inside, as in ammonites

Jurassic 193–136 million years ago

keel ridge along outer edge of ammonite

Laurasia northern supercontinent comprising North America, Europe and Asia that existed in the Mesozoic

lobe backward projection of a suture line (ammonites)

lophophore internal branching structure of a brachiopod which sets up currents for feeding and respiration

Mesozoic geological era from 225–65 million years ago consisting of the Triassic, Jurassic and Cretaceous periods

notochord stiffening rod along back, present in the development of all chordates

Ordovician 500–435 million years ago

ornithischians an order of dinosaurs characterised by the structure of the pelvis which is more advanced than in the saurischians

Palaeozoic geological era from 570–225 million years ago consisting of the Cambrian, Ordovician, Devonian, Carboniferous and Permian periods

Pangaea supercontinent comprising all the world's land mass that existed in the Permian

pedicle muscular attachment organ of a brachiopod

Permian 280–225 million years ago

petrifaction fossilisation process in which the organic remains are impregnated with minerals which increases their hardness and weight

polyp soft parts of a coral animal

Precambrian 4600–570 million years ago

protozoan single-celled animal

pygidium tail region of a trilobite

radial plates upper thecal plates (sea lilies); central or side plates (blastoids)

recrystallisation fossilisation process in which the original structure is gradually transformed into a crystalline structure

replacement fossilisation process in which the original organic remains dissolve and are replaced by minerals

saurischians an order of dinosaurs characterised by the structure of the pelvis which is more primitive than in the ornithischians

sediment deposit formed from particles derived from the erosion of rocks or by the accumulation of organic materials

Silurian 435–395 million years ago

siphuncle narrow tube running through each chamber of a cephalopod

spicules skeletal elements having one or more axes, composed of calcite or silica, as in sponges, sea cucumbers and starfishes

stipe the single branch of a graptolite colony

strata layers of rocks

stratigraphy the description, correlation and classification of bedded rocks, such as sediments and some volcanic rocks

substrate rock surface or upper layers of sediment on which organisms live

suture line along which whorls join (gastropods); region where septum meets wall of shell (cephalopods)

synapsid a sub-class of reptile characterised by a skull roof with a single opening higher than that in euryapsids in addition to those for the eyes and nostrils; all are extinct

tabulae horizontal division of corallites (corals)

taxodont dental structure of certain bivalves (clams) where numerous comb-like teeth occur along the hinge line

test the hard, calcareous wall of certain invertebrates such as echinoderms

thecal wall epitheca, outer wall of coral skeleton

therapsids mammal-like reptiles that arose in the Permian

trace fossil fossil giving indirect evidence of life (e.g. worm casts, footprints, burrows)

Triassic 225–193 million years ago

umbo in shells which grow by marginal accretion, the point where shell growth begins

zone fossil any fossil of any organism that is widely distributed and which existed for a relatively short time; useful for dating rocks

Index

Page numbers in *italics* refer to illustrations